# the new HEDGEHOG book

# the new HEDGEHOG book

## Pat Morris
### with illustrations by Guy Troughton

Whittet Books

First published 2006
Reprinted 2008, 2010 (with revisions)
Text © 2006, 2010 by Pat Morris
Illustrations © 2006 by Guy Troughton
The original *Hedgehogs* was first published in 1983 and reprinted
1984, 1985, 1987, 1990, 1992, 1994, 1995, 1998, 2001, 2003

Whittet Books Ltd, 1 St John's Lane, Stansted, Essex CM24 8JU
www.whittetbooks.com
email: mail@whittetbooks.com

**Cataloguing in publication data**
A catalogue record for this title is available from the British Library

**ISBN 978 1 873580 71 4**

The poem *Requiem for a Hedgehog*, p. 132, reprinted by kind
permission of Avon Wildlife

# Contents

*This book has been approved by hedgehogs.*

## Acknowledgments

Countless people have contributed in small ways to my knowledge of hedgehogs and to maintaining my interest in them. Much information contained in this book has also been gleaned from the research reports of other biologists in Britain and abroad. My students Paul Bright, Simone Bullion, Samantha Craig-Wood, Warren Cresswell, Richard Leishman, Kathy Meakin, Samantha Munn, Nigel Reeve, Susan Sharafi, Ruth Temple, Hugh Warwick, Andy Wroot and many others have collectively devoted thousands of hours to helping me investigate what hedgehogs get up to. I am especially grateful to them for their fortitude and for what they have spared me having to do for myself. I am also grateful to Mr and Mrs R. Wall for letting us intrude into their garden, interfere with their hedgehogs and generally make a nuisance of ourselves in the dead of night for more than five years. The kind and unstinting co-operation of the authorities responsible for a Royal Park and a West London golf course has provided us with ideal study sites for some of the few major field investigations of hedgehog ecology in Britain. Similarly I owe much to certain gamekeepers for saving dead hedgehogs for me and to long-suffering friends like Dr Derek Yalden for undertaking studies of bits removed from the hedgehogs thus obtained. I am also grateful to my mother for typing the original text of this book and before that the PhD thesis and a score or more papers and magazine articles from which the book has drawn extensively. Some of my studies on hedgehogs have been aided by funds from the Universities Federation for Animal Welfare, the People's Trust for Endangered Species, the Mammal Society, the RSPCA and several generous individuals. The British Hedgehog Preservation Society has also been very helpful in providing financial support for hedgehog studies. I am grateful to them all.

*Pat Morris*

# Preface

Everyone has a soft spot for the hedgehog. It is one of the most instantly recognized animals and yet one of the most poorly studied British mammals. Many people put out food for their hedgehogs and want to know more about these intriguing creatures, yet there are few books that one can turn to for reliable information.

Nowadays there are many people who specialise in looking after sick and injured hedgehogs and are happy to help with enquiries, but it wasn't always so. During the early 1960s, there seemed to be nobody working on wild hedgehogs at all and nobody for the media and the public to consult when they had hedgehog questions to ask. I had begun to investigate hedgehog winter nesting behaviour as a result of some illicit activity that had led me to discover where they spent the winter months. Later, as an undergraduate student, I attended a mammal course at which one of the tutors mentioned that nobody really knew much what hedgehogs did in the winter. When I said, 'I do!' he encouraged me to investigate further. I later went on to study hedgehogs full-time for three years as the topic of my PhD thesis. Word got around that I 'knew about hedgehogs', reinforced by various radio and TV appearances. I became 'Mr Hedgehog' and soon I was getting lengthy phone calls and piles of letters which took up a lot of my time which ought to have been spent dealing with my students at Royal Holloway (University of London). So I decided that I would write a simple book that would answer all the commonest questions in one go, to save me all that letter writing. Since hedgehogs are fun things as well as serious animals, I wanted the book to be fun too, with jokes as well as serious stuff. But various publishers couldn't understand this, saying that I should either write a joke book or a serious study, not some kind of weird hybrid. Finally, Annabel Whittet agreed to try this format and it made her famous. Soon other books followed in similar style.

*Hedgehogs* was first published in 1983, illustrated with informative and charming drawings by Guy Troughton, one of many Royal Holloway students who became involved in various forms of hedgehogging. He managed brilliantly to capture the fun as well as the serious, and the format he created proved very popular. Over 30,000 copies of the book have been distributed, with translations into several other European languages too. A revised edition was issued in 1994, but much has happened since then. So, this *New Hedgehogs Book* aims to incorporate all the basic information contained in the original volume, because it doesn't go out of date, and also adds a bit more as a result of further studies and developments that have taken place over the past 20 years or so.

This book aims to provide simple, factual and down-to-earth information in sufficient quantity and detail to be useful, but not overwhelming. It should be suitable for reading all at once or dipped into as and when interest or need dictates. It's meant to reflect the fun and interest of hedgehogs; it's not a textbook. Many people will have their own observations and hedgehog stories and may feel that a lot has been left out, but this book is not intended to be an encyclopaedia. A more comprehensive review has been written by another of my students, Nigel Reeve (Reeve, 1994), a book I should have written myself, but was too busy with other university work and with trying to organise new research on dormice. There is indeed much more to be said about hedgehogs. There is also a lot more to be learned. However, it is often dangerous to generalize, especially about hedgehogs, based on only a few observations. Unfortunately, quite a lot of the new hedgehog experts now available offer forthright opinions or advice that is often not founded on sound scientific research. When more studies have been done in more different places we will be in a stronger position to give definitive answers to questions about the natural history of the hedgehog.

I have now retired from my university post and the hedgehog baton will have to be carried forward by someone else. Meanwhile, this book serves as a summary of where we are at in relation to knowledge about hedgehogs at the start of the 21st century. I hope you find it interesting, informative and enjoyable.

*Dr Pat Morris, 2010*

# What's in a name?

The name 'hedgehog' is definitely of English origin, but seems to have come into use about 1450. The old Anglo Saxon name was *il*, evidently derived from the German word *igel*, still used there today, like *egel* in the Netherlands and *igelkott* in Sweden. Other names clearly refer to the animal's distinctive spines (e.g. *pindsvin* in Danish). Country folk often call the hedgehog 'urchin', a word which seems to be derived from Norman French. In the past there have been many other country names used for the hedgehog, 'hedgepig' and 'furzepig' being perhaps the best known, but few of these are in use today. The animal also has its own name in Gaelic (the rather uncomplimentary *graineog* meaning 'horrible one'), in Welsh and in old Cornish.

The Latin word for hedgehog is *Erinaceus* and was chosen in 1758 by the Swedish naturalist Linnaeus to be henceforth the scientific name by which the hedgehog and its kin would be known throughout the world in the classification of the animal kingdom.

Hedgehogs pop up in the writings of William Shakespeare in *The Tempest* and *Midsummer Night's Dream*; elsewhere he calls them 'hedgepigs' and 'urchins', but at least we know what he was talking about. Citations in the Bible are more problematical and biblical scholars have argued at length about the hedgehog's inclusion in the scriptures. The difficulty seems to be due to ambiguity in translations. The Hebrew word *kippod* is rendered as 'hedgehog' in some English versions of the Bible and 'bittern' in others. The difference could hardly be greater and there seems to be no way of sorting out just what is really meant. The only certainty is that there are indeed hedgehogs (and bitterns!) to be found in the Holy Land and so hedgehogs could quite properly be called biblical animals and must have been familiar to biblical people.

Nowadays we can carry out computerised searches for the word 'hedgehog' and if you do that in a special search of the scientific literature, to see what studies have been done on the animal, you get a lot of references to genetics research! The reason is not that hedgehog genetics have suddenly become popular, few studies have been made in fact. It's because someone has named a protein

in fruit flies 'hedgehog', perhaps because the gene that enables its production is carried on a special group of chromosomes that have a spiky appearance under the microscope. The substance is important in controlling growth and development. A similar substance found in vertebrates has been named 'sonic hedgehog', after the cartoon character, and may be linked with cancer control, hence the flurry of research in this area.

## Hedgehogs, people and popularity

In the quarter century since the first edition of this book was published there has been a huge surge in public interest in the hedgehog. Often it seems motivated by compassion for what looks like an odd and helpless creature, beset by the dangers of the modern world. Whereas at one time I used to be the only source of advice on hedgehogs, now there is help at hand on every side. I used to get a lot of phone calls asking how to help injured hedgehogs, now there are literally scores of kindly people who specialise in providing care and advice in such circumstances. This has been a relief to me as I could not justify spending half an hour of university time listening to a tearful woman on the phone from Devon saying her hedgehog was ill, yet I could scarcely tell her to go away.

One kindly lady, having raised her own family, decided to build an extension to her house as a hedgehog hospital. I was asked to make a speech at the opening ceremony, followed by the Vicar who blessed

# Sonic the hedgehog

This is the name of a computer game released by Sega of America in 1991 and it made them famous. It stars a high-powered hedgehog with attitude called Sonic who tears about the screen, jumping through obstacles with incredible speed. The game was technically very advanced for its day and quickly attracted a huge following. Nowadays Sonic inspires websites, toys, comics, movies, music and computer screen 'wallpaper'. He even gets sold on ebay as a collector's item. There's a whole Sonic world out there, that fuddy-duddies like me find both bewildering and completely barmy. The point of the original game was simple enough and focussed on Dr Robotnik. He captured lots of Sonic's animal friends, trapping them inside robots. The incredible Sonic could free his pals by destroying the robots with his spinning attacks. Meanwhile, the evil Robotnik is after some 'chaos emeralds' and Sonic must get them before he does. It's pretty daft really, but who cares? The real problem is that Sonic's picture shows that he is actually more like some kind of squirrel than a hedgehog!

the enterprise. This is surely in the best traditions of the British being kind to animals. It's good that so much attention is given to sickly hogs nowadays, although many scientists say it's a waste of time. After all what is the real benefit of saving just a few individuals, or even hundreds of them? This may be true for mice, where saving a few from an early death really does make little difference to the population. Mice produce large families and do so several times per year, and some of the progeny may themselves breed in the same season. A female mouse may be responsible for 20-30 young per year. If one is lost, there are plenty more. But the hedgehog is a species that produces few young, and every one is precious, especially when there are so many dangers on every side; whatever we do to assist increased survival is worthwhile. Besides, insisting that we should let Nature take its course ignores people's feelings. If people want to assist apparently helpless animals, then they should be allowed to do so, provided that the animals themselves do actually benefit (see pp 89, 92). Moreover, the publicity generated by apparently trivial stories serves to maintain people's awareness of wildlife issues and the threats that animals face in the modern countryside. This cannot be a bad thing when most people live in towns, largely out of touch with the natural world.

In 1982, the BBC broadcast a film called 'The Great Hedgehog Mystery', a charming investigation of folklore about this animal. It proved very popular, although I squirm at my own contribution. Its producer, Dilys Breese, reported that it had been seen by 12.7 million people, 24.7% of the entire viewing population! Another sign of massive public support comes in the form of the 11,000 people who are members of the British Hedgehog Preservation Society (BHPS). This was started in 1982 by Major Adrian Coles, a colourful local councillor in Shropshire. He captured public imagination by beginning a campaign to get landowners and local authorities to build escape ramps into cattle grids. There was huge support for him and his efforts to promote hedgehog welfare, with constant stories in the press. One Canadian newspaper commented that, from a transatlantic perspective, Britain appeared to have achieved two major successes in 1982 – namely evicting the Argentine army from the Falkland Islands and saving hedgehogs from cattle grids!

The BHPS went on to produce information leaflets and used the hedgehog to raise awareness of wildlife issues among schoolchildren. It also supported hedgehog research, particularly on the fate of rehabilitated animals, although never had the funds to pay for major projects. The first BHPS grant of £1,000 was to support some of my field studies. The money came in the form of a large cheque over 60 cm

# The Christmas hedgehog

Sometime in the 1990s the hedgehog seems to have been promoted to a special section of the Animal Kingdom, along with dolphins and otters. These animals are regarded as very familiar and are enormously popular with the public, although relatively few people have ever actually seen one. They are creatures that can do no wrong. Hedgehogs joined a select group that includes the robin, the ultimate familiar and blameless creature. They started to appear on Christmas cards! It will be interesting to see whether their elevation to the status of an animal god is permanent or whether, after a while, they fade from the Christmas scene. Hedgehogs do occur in the Holy Land, but have no relevance to the Christmas story, being in hibernation at the time, but never mind eh?

long. I phoned the college finance officer and asked if I could bring him 'a big cheque'. He was delighted, thinking I meant lots of money, but his face was a picture when I showed him the massive sheet of paper. He was at a loss to know what to do with it, since it didn't fit into any of his envelopes or filing cabinets.

At one time, the BHPS used to notify its members who lived within about 20 miles of anywhere that I was giving a hedgehog lecture so they could attend if they wished. One evening I arrived at a local Women's Institute to give my talk and found that the audience was about double the expected size. The WI contingent couldn't understand where all the extra people had come from, and the other half of the audience couldn't understand why a hedgehog lecture was accompanied by sale of jam tarts and began with a rousing rendition of 'Jerusalem'!

# Mrs Tiggywinkle

This famous and homely creature began life in 1901 in a bedtime story by Beatrix Potter. Mrs T lived in a small cave up in the Lake District, taking in washing for her neighbours. The story has Lucie, a local farmer's daughter, searching the fells for a lost handkerchief. She stumbles upon Mrs Tiggywinkle washing a scarlet waistcoat for Cock Robin and stockings for Sally Henny Penny, then ends up helping to distribute piles of sparkling clean laundry to the neighbours. Today you can visit the Newlands Valley and walk the same Fells as Lucie did, passing the old lead mine entrances that might once have housed Mrs Tiggywinkle's washhouse and the bubbling springs from which she might once have collected her water in an egg cup. Down in Bowness on Windermere you might also meet a latter day Mrs Tiggywinkle at 'The World of Beatrix Potter' and you can certainly visit the Potter household at 'Hilltop', a 17th century farmhouse now owned by the National Trust.

# Evolution: the hedgehog's pedigree and family history

Our modern hedgehogs have no really close relatives among other mammals. They have distant links with moles, shrews and certain foreign animals which are grouped together and called 'the Insectivora'. This is a bit misleading because many of them feed on things other than insects and they are often very dissimilar in appearance.

In fact hedgehogs are an animal family all on their own. The modern forms simply evolved from more ancient ones and have been a separate evolutionary line for millions of years. The first hedgehogs probably appeared over 15 million years ago, long before sabre-toothed tigers, woolly rhinos, mammoths and other modern upstarts. Those creatures are now extinct, but the hedgehog is with us still. It's as though the Mark 1 hedgehog was sufficiently well adapted to its way of life that nothing better has yet evolved to replace it. There have been a few evolutionary experiments, like a pig-sized Mediterranean hedgehog; but they didn't work and the various species of modern hedgehogs are all much the same size and shape as our own. Just because our hedgehog has been around for a long time, it doesn't mean that it has always been found in Britain. During the past million years there have been several major ice ages, during which the hedgehog must have retreated to the warmer parts of the Continent, then re-invaded when the climate improved. This was no problem to a land animal so long as Britain retained a land connection with Europe. That was lost when rising sea levels, caused by melting ice at the end of the last glaciation, finally isolated Britain as an island about 9,000 years ago. By then hedgehogs were well established here, along with Stone Age Man and his successors.

Because the hedgehog has such an ancient lineage and has had so little reason to change, it retains many primitive features that were probably characteristic of the very earliest mammals of all. The teeth, feet and skeleton for example are all very basic. The senses and brain, centred on smell rather than vision, are similarly very primitive though no less useful for all that.

# Similarity is only skin-deep

The most obvious characteristic of the hedgehog is its spiny coat. This naturally leads people to assume that it is related to other conspicuously spiny animals such as porcupines. But jumping to such a simple conclusion is like assuming that a judge is similar to a beauty queen because both seem to have long curly hair – appearances can be deceptive! In fact porcupines are rodents (like rats, squirrels and guinea pigs) with fundamental differences between them and hedgehogs, resulting from a completely separate evolutionary history. Other spiny creatures include spiny rats from South America, spiny mice from Africa, as well as Australian spiny anteaters and some spiny Madagascan things called tenrecs. All of these evolved spines independently, superficially similar to those of hedgehogs, but actually less complex and not so well developed. When fundamentally dissimilar creatures evolve a similar structure and begin to resemble each other in appearance, biologists refer to the phenomenon as 'convergent evolution'. The copy-cat evolution of spines in various groups of mammals is one of the best examples of this.

*Porcupine*          *Echidna or spiny anteater*

*Spiny mouse of Africa*          *Tenrec*

# Hedgehog species

The hedgehogs form a distinctive family of about a dozen or so species. These include five kinds of hairy hedgehogs or 'moon rats' which live in S.E. Asia and don't have any spines. The different species of typical spiny hedgehogs look very similar and differ from our British one in relatively minor respects (e.g. in having black and white spines, longer ears or white belly fur). They are classified into four groups of species (called 'genera'). Two of these, *Atelerix* and *Paraechinus*, include a total of seven species, mostly living in Africa, with two of the *Paraechinus* species extending into the Middle East and India. The genus *Hemiechinus* (long-eared hedgehogs) has four species that are widespread across the dry areas of western and central Asia. The remaining genus, *Erinaceus*, is the one to which the British or brown-chested hedgehog belongs. Our own British hedgehog, scientifically known as *Erinaceus europaeus*, is the same species that occurs throughout most of the Continent. In eastern Europe and across into Russia, the local hedgehogs typically are bigger than ours and have a white chest. This and some other minor features mean that they are classified as a different species, *Erinaceus concolor*. A third, closely related, species *(Erinaceus amurensis)* lives in China.

Throughout Europe, hedgehogs are found in farmland, forest and fragmented suburban habitats. They live up mountains, at least to the tree line, but don't care for wet places like marshes. In very dry areas, especially in some of the Mediterranean countries, another species (from North Africa) is found. In the north, hedgehogs occur up to about 60° N latitude; approximately the limit of deciduous trees across southern Scandinavia and Finland.

'Our' hedgehog was also introduced from Britain to New Zealand in the nineteenth century by homesick settlers anxious to make their new country as familiar as the old homeland. Hedgehogs are now doing very nicely there (see p. 24), but they have not been introduced successfully to any other distant places. There are no hedgehogs in North or South America, nor in Australia for example. However, they have been released on various islands around the British coast, where their presence has sometimes become rather controversial (as discussed later in this book).

Erinaceus or European type hedgehogs

Atelerix algirus or Algerian Hedgehog

Atelerix and Paraechinus or African hedgehogs

Hemiechinus or Long-eared hedgehogs

*World distribution of hedgehogs*

# The hedgehog in Britain

In Britain, the hedgehog is one of our more widely distributed species. It is found almost everywhere, but tends to be scarce or absent from wet areas and it also seems not to like extensive pine forests. Upland habitats such as moorland and mountainsides are not very popular either, probably because they lack both suitable food and suitable nesting places. Unlike the mole, the common shrew, and some other British mammals, the hedgehog does occur in Ireland and is quite common there.

Hedgehogs are also found on various Scottish islands, posing the question of how they got there. These islands have not been linked to the mainland since before the last Ice Age, and so their hedgehogs could not have arrived on foot. Nor are they likely to have swum to places like Orkney and Shetland (or to other islands such as Jersey or the Isles of Wight or Man). Their presence must be due to introductions by humans. You might think that nobody would bother taking hedgehogs by boat to such places (although people get very attached to their pet hedgehogs); but this animal is quite likely to be carted about accidentally. It normally hides away in the daytime (and overwinter), often choosing such places as hay or brushwood piles for concealment. It would be very easy indeed to scoop up a heap of peat 'turves' or thatching material, complete with hedgehog inside, and carry it away, literally, 'over the sea to Skye'. Many of the Scottish islands lack fuel, building materials and animal fodder; so regular forays to the mainland have probably been quite normal for perhaps thousands of years. The accidental importation of hedgehogs and other animals is not only explicable, but almost inevitable. More recently, hedgehogs have been deliberately transported to other islands, usually in an attempt to control garden pests.

As a matter of principle, animals should never be introduced to islands from which they are naturally absent because of the damage they might do to other species. Ground-nesting birds are particularly vulnerable and need the security of islands for their own survival. Nevertheless, between 1970 and 1990, small numbers of hedgehogs were released on various islands off the British coast. In 1985, two pairs were imported to Sark in the Channel Islands at the express request of the island's principal lady, the Seigneur's wife, and became very abundant there within a few years. Two others were taken in the same year to the Isles of Scilly, where they quickly became common on St Mary's. At some time fairly recently a few were released on Alderney in the Channel Islands and, notoriously, hedgehogs also took over the island of North Ronaldsay in the Orkneys, and the Hebridean islands of North and South Uist, following introductions there in the 1970s. Hedgehogs were first reported from Brownsea Island (in Poole harbour) in 1968, and by 1981 the population had increased to an estimated 100 plus. However, in this case it is just possible that they had swum to the island as it is quite close to the shore.

Although it is true that hedgehogs are found almost everywhere on the mainland, they are probably not equally abundant in all areas. It is difficult to be scientific about this because we have no reliable way of measuring hedgehog numbers. However, my surveys suggest that more hedgehogs are killed per 100 miles of road in the North East than in the South West or South East regions. Curiously, there are also large numbers killed in East Anglia, where the enormous arable fields appear to be highly unsuitable habitat. But that may be exactly why so many get run over. The hedgehogs are forced to live along the grassy road verges, and risk being squashed, precisely because the fields offer them little food and no shelter.

A notable feature of the hedgehog's distribution in Britain is its abundance in urban and suburban habitats. In the London area, for example, hedgehogs are found well into the inner suburbs (e.g. Willesden, Hampstead, West Ham, Deptford, Streatham, Wimbledon) and there are still permanent populations in some of the central London parks (such as Hyde Park and Regent's Park). Presumably it was a member of the St James's Park population who was reported by *The Times* to have been caught years ago exploring the Admiralty building in Whitehall!

The abundance of hedgehogs in suburbia is not only a pleasure to the people who live there, but also a source of optimism about the future. We tend to contemplate gloomily the expansion of urban sprawl into the countryside, assuming that this cancerous growth automatically obliterates all wildlife. Whereas this may indeed be a serious threat to some animals, it is clear that the hedgehog is less troubled by the spread of bricks and mortar. Indeed the complex of parks, gardens, cemeteries, railway land and waste ground is much to its liking – especially as the human inhabitants of the houses insist on putting out masses of free food. Admittedly some of this is actually intended for pets and for birds; but it's good stuff for hedgehogs too and a shame to see it wasted on overfed cats. The features that make surburbia inconvenient for many animals (disturbance, garden fences, lack of hiding places, etc.) are not a problem for hedgehogs who prosper and multiply. Many suburban gardens are too small to support hedgehogs, but remember that, although we may feel confined

*Presence of hedgehogs in Britain*

by fences and garden hedges, hedgehogs are not. A tiny 10m x 5m garden is indeed too small to support a hedgehog, but if it backs on to another garden and has a row either side the total area available to hedgehogs may be quite considerable. If a garden is entirely walled in or surrounded by a totally impermeable fence, then hedgehogs will have to give it a miss, but few fences lack holes of some sort and a hedgehog's nightly wanderings will often be governed by where the gates and fence holes are. Indeed they may forage along a road verge or field edge, making separate excursions into each garden as they pass the gate.

Any animal that can come to terms with suburbia, our one major expanding habitat, has a great advantage over the many species that suffer so much these days from habitat destruction. The hedgehog's success in and around towns is not just a pleasant surprise, but surely a valuable safeguard and insurance for its future survival. However, a worrying development during the 1980s was 'urban infill'. Rising house prices made it worthwhile for developers to buy a couple of old houses with big rambling gardens, clear the lot and build a dozen neo-Georgian 'executive dwellings' in their place. Converting big old gardens into little tidy ones must have deprived a great many urban hedgehogs of ideal habitat. Moreover, the fashion for patios, 'decking' and general smartness (fuelled by trendy TV programmes) has resulted in large areas of suburbia being too sanitised and tidy for hedgehogs to prosper. Progressively they are likely to have died out, leaving a few living in isolated patches. These mini populations are probably too small to be viable and piecemeal extinction is likely. Many people tell me that they no longer get hedgehogs coming to their gardens, even though nothing has changed in years. The problem is that if the surroundings change, the hedgehogs just die out. I have not had a hedgehog in my own garden for more than ten years now.

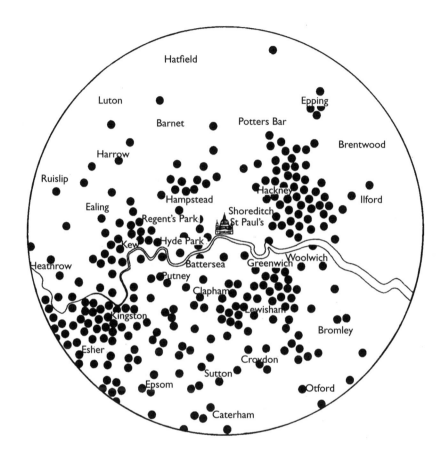

Hatfield
Luton
Barnet
Potters Bar
Epping
Brentwood
Harrow
Ruislip
Hampstead
Hackney
Ilford
Ealing
Shoreditch
Regent's Park
St Paul's
Kew
Hyde Park
Heathrow
Battersea
Greenwich
Woolwich
Putney
Clapham
Lewisham
Kingston
Bromley
Esher
Croydon
Sutton
Otford
Epsom
Caterham

*This map shows a twenty-mile circle round St Paul's, indicating areas in which hedgehogs were recorded in the 1960s. They are probably found in some of the blank areas too, except possibly in the very centre; unfortunately the necessary surveys haven't been repeated, so we have no recent data. The demolition of large houses and resultant use of the site and garden for several smaller ones has changed extensive areas of London for the worst. Hedgehog populations must be severely fragmented as a result. It is unlikely that their distribution in London now is as continuous or as widespread as this map shows.*

# The hedgehog in New Zealand

Apart from a few bats, no mammals ever managed to reach New Zealand naturally, they were all brought by humans. First came people, about 800 years ago, swiftly followed by their dogs and rats. Captain Cook brought farm animals five centuries later. European settlers found the lack of familiar animals both unwelcome and unhelpful. They set about importing various species to hunt and to make the place seem more like home. New Zealand's first hedgehogs were a pair that arrived aboard the good ship *Hydaspes* in 1870, with further batches sent from Britain over the next 15 years or so. At first they were imported as reminders of home, but later became appreciated as potential destroyers of garden pests, especially slugs and snails. They were particularly useful in grassy areas, where a hedgehog might consume up to 850 'grass grubs' in a night, reducing the population of these damaging pests by 40% in the summer. This is important in New Zealand because pastureland is so valuable there, being the basic support for the vital sheep and dairy industries. As in Britain, the NZ hedgehogs ate lots of slugs, but few snails (especially the larger ones). They also rejected woodlice, just as they do here.

Hedgehogs in New Zealand seem to be smaller on average than those in Britain, which are in turn smaller than those of Germany and Scandinavia. About half have natural dental anomalies, such as missing teeth, three times as many as is normal in Britain. They seem to manage perfectly well just the same, suggesting that vets and animal carers need not worry too much about missing teeth. The New Zealand hedgehogs have no fleas (again showing that they can manage perfectly well without!), but mange mites are a much more serious problem than in European hedgehogs and may even be a significant cause of mortality. Fewer than one hedgehog in a hundred carries TB, so the danger of them transmitting the disease to New Zealand's cattle is nothing like as great as for the imported Australian possums, nor badgers in Britain (where 20% of them may be infected).

In the warmer parts of North Island (where the temperatures are similar to those of Spain, but the rainfall is more generous), the hedgehogs enjoy ideal conditions. Hibernation lasts only about three months and some hedgehogs may not hibernate at all. Further south, in the cool parts of South Island, the winters are relatively cold and hibernation is more prolonged. This does confirm that hibernation is a flexible response to weather conditions and that hibernation dates can be highly variable (see p. 145). Shorter winters also mean that there is time for females to have two litters per year. This has helped the population to expand rapidly in just a few decades. The longer breeding season and lower winter mortality effectively mean hogs are more numerous in New Zealand, despite litter size and longevity being similar to those in Britain.

Hedgehogs became very widespread and abundant on both islands. Further imports and spreading of batches within New Zealand ensured that hedgehogs had colonised almost everywhere that was suitable by 1972, within 100 years of their arrival. Hedgehogs are still rare in the mountains and the very wet areas of South Island (where they get 6 metres of rain in a year!). They are especially frequent in farmland and gardens, but scarce in forested areas. Favourable areas may have up to 2.5 hogs per hectare, more than twice what we expect to find in Britain.

In 1987 I went to inspect the New Zealand hedgehogs and counted 636 dead ones as I drove 6,000 miles. In terms of hedgehogs per mile, that's at least three times more than we usually see in Britain. On some roads there you could stand on one dead hedgehog and almost see the next!

North Island had the most dead on roads, but several surveys

(including mine) show there are always fewer in South Island. The worrying thing is that there seems to be a declining trend. Bob Brockie, the Father of New Zealand hedgehog research, has counted roadkills regularly for years. He found an average of 25 per 100km in 1956, 10.8 in 1984, 7.7 in 1994 and only 1.7 in 2005. He began with at least ten times more than in Britain and other parts of Europe, at a similar time, and ended with a figure that was barely twice the British roadkill count in 2004 (0.8 per 100km). What's going on downunder?

# Hedgehog crisps

In 1981, a pub owner in Wales decided as a lark to market 'Hedgehog Crisps', but ran into trouble with many animal lovers who believed that they were made from real hedgehogs (they weren't, just pork flavoured). Officialdom was not amused either and he was prosecuted for false advertising, precisely because they were not actually made from hedgehogs! They were then sold as 'hedgehog flavoured' crisps after a panel of gypsies had been called in to decide what flavour they thought was most appropriate. Hedgehog crisps have now evolved into a fully fledged brand name for organic potato crisps. There is a cheese and tomato option, and a sea salt and cider vinegar flavoured version, hailed on the packet as 'The Dawning of a New Crisp Era'. Sales now amount to about £2 million worth every year.

And talking of pubs, why are there so few named 'The Hedgehog'? There is one in Suffolk, but nobody there seemed to know how it got its name.

# The hedgehog's body:
# the outside

There's no mistaking a hedgehog for anything else. It's Britain's only spiny mammal. This particular feature and the persuasive resemblance to a clockwork toy mean that we instantly recognize a hedgehog for what it is and do not closely inspect the details of its anatomy. For example, have you ever noticed a hedgehog's tail? Are you sure it's got one? In fact there is a tail and it's about an inch (2cm) long.

You don't normally see a hedgehog's legs and feet either, so that when it's walking slowly it seems to be trundling along on wheels.

*How long are a hedgehog's legs? Long enough to reach the ground!*

Actually the legs are quite long, 4"(10 cm) from hip to toe, but normally hidden under a 'skirt' formed by the long hairs at the edge of the spiny part of the skin along the flanks. The voluminous, loose skin acts almost like a bell tent, or a nun's habit, hiding all that's underneath, especially when the hedgehog is 'slumped down', so to

*Powerful forefoot and claws for digging*

*Footprints: fore* (left) *and hind* (right)

speak. If it wants to move fast, it can raise itself up, extend its legs and show a clean pair of heels – literally. As it walks off, the heels are visible from the rear. The hind feet are about 1½"(3-4 cm) long and rather narrow. The front feet are shorter but usually broader, so the two leave distinctly different footprints on mud or clean surfaces. The tracks then seem to have been made by two animals, but they aren't – just front and back of the same one.

The hedgehog's vital statistics change somewhat with age, just as they do in humans: old hedgehogs often tend to be big and fat; and males tend to be bigger than females. Body weight is one of the hedgehog's most variable features, but also one of the most helpful in giving us clues about age and health. One-year-old hedgehogs usually weigh about 1-2lb(450-680g); heavier ones are normally older.

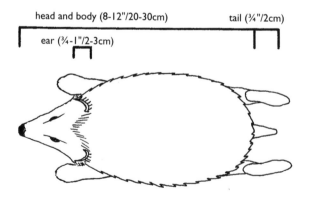

head and body (8-12"/20-30cm)    tail (¾"/2cm)

ear (¾-1"/2-3cm)

However, weight varies greatly with the seasons. A one-year-old animal may double its weight in the course of its second summer as it lays down fat for hibernation. Body weight is very much governed by abundance of food. Early in the year, when fat reserves are exhausted and there is little natural food to be found, some adults may weigh only 12oz(350g) (like a 6-stone man) and are badly in need of food. When well fed, British hedgehogs can grow to well over 2lb (1,500g or more) in the wild, but pet hedgehogs with indulgent owners can just grow and grow. The biggest I ever saw was 'Georgie', who weighed over 4.5lb (2.2 kg): a giant among hogs. I heard of another called 'Fred' who was just about to eat his 800th boiled egg, bringing him to about 3lb 3oz (1,800g). Hedgehogs on the Continent are much bigger than ours, and even wild hedgehogs there seem to attain similarly massive proportions without help.

## The spines and skin
The spines are a hedgehog's most distinctive characteristic. They are just modified hairs, about 1"(2-3 cm) long and $^1/_{10}$"(2 mm) in diameter. They taper to a very sharp point at one end. At the other end, the spine narrows, bends through about 60° at the narrowest point – the 'neck' of the spine – and then ends in a hemispherical bulb, which is buried in the skin. This arrangement means that if the hedgehog is struck a blow or falls heavily on to its spines, the force is absorbed by bending the springy spine 'necks'. Moreover, the ball

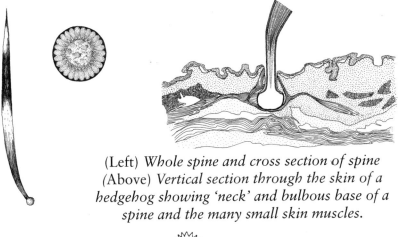

(Left) *Whole spine and cross section of spine*
(Above) *Vertical section through the skin of a hedgehog showing 'neck' and bulbous base of a spine and the many small skin muscles.*

buried in the skin forms a big blunt end that stops the spine being forced back into the animal's own flesh. Inside, the spines are hollow with strengthening ridges running down the inside walls of the tube. This provides a very strong and rigid structure with little weight.

Each spine is a creamy white, shading to brown at the base and pure white at the tip. Just behind the sharp end is a dark band, usually chocolate brown, which gives the spiny coat an overall grizzled appearance. In young hedgehogs (and occasional old ones too) the dark band is almost black, giving a very contrasty look to the spines. It is quite common for a few individual spines to be all-white (often in younger animals), and some hedgehogs have patches of white spines, a characteristic which can probably be inherited. Occasionally we see hedgehogs all of whose spines are white or yellowish, making the animal look like a ghost. These are just pale colour variants; in other

*Spines erected* (left) *and relaxed* (right)

respects they are quite normal, having brown hairs, dark feet and black eyes. Technically these pale blonde varieties are called 'leucistic'. They are rare on the mainland, but on Alderney (one of the Channel Islands), a quarter of the population is like this. A possible reason is that hedgehogs are not native to Alderney and were introduced there sometime in the recent past. One story is that a few were purchased from Harrod's in London. The founding population would therefore have been only perhaps two pairs. For the first few generations,

*How does a darts player score 800 with one throw? Answer: throw a hedgehog at the dart board.*

inbreeding would have been unavoidable, with males mating with their own daughters for example. In such circumstances, if one of the original animals had carried a recessive gene for 'blondness' it would have been consolidated within the population and caused about a quarter of the animals to show pale features – just as we see today. The Alderney hedgehogs are so special that they feature on local postage stamps and postcards.

True albinos are sometimes seen among mainland hedgehogs. These have no dark colouration anywhere, not even a black nose, and their eyes are characteristically pale pink. Probably fewer than one in 10,000 hedgehogs deviates so markedly from the normal colouration, and white hedgehogs are probably rarer than white moles. Whereas some mammals (e.g. squirrels and mice) occasionally produce all-black colour varieties, hedgehogs never do. I have actually seen blue ones and an orange one too, but these were a consequence of tangling with newly painted garden fences.

In 1898 a Professor Fritsch reported to a scientific society that he had obtained a spineless variety of the hedgehog. He exhibited a stuffed specimen and published a photograph of it. But I suspect that someone had been pulling Herr Professor's leg. His specimen was a hedgehog all right, you can see the distinctive teeth in his photograph, but the lack of spines was more likely to have been due to a mischievous taxidermist than a natural phenomenon. Nevertheless, I have myself seen two completely naked hedgehogs, lacking both fur and spines, which seemed to be the result of some kind of genetic abnormality. One was called 'Alice' and she had been spiny when young, but lost them all as she grew. She was a pinkish grey all over, with a few scattered hairs and obviously very vulnerable without her protection. She actually lived for six years, but only because she was kept safely indoors. The other bald hedgehog I met had been christened 'the Blob'. This one was white all over and

*A flea can leap many times its own height.*

looked very weird, like a close relative of a haggis! There were no spines, hairs or whiskers, not even claws. Clearly the mechanism for manufacturing keratin (the protein the forms all these structures) had failed, almost certainly a genetic defect. Sadly, soon after I made its acquaintance, the Blob escaped from its owner. It was probably eaten by something almost immediately, effectively removing its genes from the breeding pool and reducing the chance of ever seeing such a thing again.

Hedgehogs are not spiny on the underside of course (otherwise they couldn't roll up). The chest, throat, belly and legs are all covered by a long and rather coarse grey-brown fur. Where this meets the spiny area, along the flanks, the fur is extra long and shaggy. This creates the impression of a skirt, fringing the edge of the hedgehog's body. The belly fur is very sparse and you can easily see the skin through it, not like in rabbits or cats for example. This must make it a chilly business for the hedgehog to forage in frosty conditions or in dew-laden grass, especially as its spiny parts have no soft fur at all. Hedgehogs are unusual in having so little insulation for their bodies. On the other hand coarse, sparse hair does not get clogged by mud like an ordinary mammal's fur, nor will it collect plant burrs or become heavily saturated with wet. Perhaps the advantages of a hairy belly, for one so close to the ground, outweigh the disadvantages of heat loss and discomfort.

# How many spines does a hedgehog have?

By the time a baby hedgehog leaves its mother's nest, it has about 3,000 spines on its back. As it grows older and bigger, more spines are added to maintain a suitable density of them. Consequently an average adult hedgehog weighing about 1lb 5oz(600g) has 5,000 or so spines. A very big animal, over twice that size, might have 7,500. Some books suggest that hedgehogs may have 16,000 spines, but this is an exaggerated figure, probably based on a faulty method of estimation. That many spines would be a heavy burden to carry around. I know my figures are correct because I cut them off dead hedgehogs and counted them all.

# Do hedgehogs moult?

All mammals have hair and it is normal to moult periodically as a means of getting rid of old hairs and replacing them with new ones. The hedgehog's relatives, the moles and shrews, moult twice per year. The long, thick winter coat is shed in spring to be replaced by summer fur. In the autumn, this is lost and a new winter coat is grown as longer denser fur becomes more necessary. The hedgehog is less concerned to keep itself warm in winter and would find it highly inconvenient to moult all its spines twice a year; they would take too long to replace. In practice, hedgehogs moult the same way that we humans do. Each hair and spine follicle has its own rate of growth and is not synchronized with its neighbours. So spines and hairs are being grown and lost continuously, one or two at a time, not in a big co-ordinated seasonal moult. In shrews and moles an individual hair has a 'service life' of only six months till the next moult. In few mammals do the individual hairs persist longer than a year. By contrast, each of the hedgehog's spines may last well over a year, perhaps more than 18 months, before it finally falls out and a replacement is grown.

# The hedgehog's body: the inside

Most of the anatomical interest of the hedgehog is on the outside, in its spines and skin. Inside, the body is equipped with a standard set of mammal bones and guts, which are fairly unremarkable. In fact the skeleton is so ordinary and unspecialized that it resembles in many ways that of the simplest prototype mammals that existed over 50 million years ago. The feet all have five toes and the forearm contains two separate bones, features that are lost or at least modified in more highly evolved mammals. The principal variation from the norm in the skeleton is the shortness of the neck, although it still contains the same number of vertebrae (7) as other mammals, including humans and giraffes. Presumably this makes it easier for the hedgehog to roll up into a compact ball.

The skull is broad and strong, squared-off at the front and with well formed cheek bones (in contrast to the skulls of relatives like shrews and moles). The teeth are very odd. The two big incisors at the front of the lower jaw (used for picking up prey) lie almost flat and point forwards instead of upwards. They don't therefore form a sharp cutting edge: one reason why the hedgehog's bite is pretty harmless. In the upper jaw, there is a big gap between the front teeth:

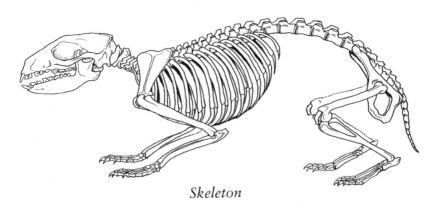

*Skeleton*

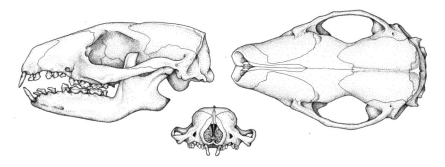

*Skull: seen from the side, above and front*

another reason for not fearing a nasty bite from them. What appear to be large canine teeth sticking down from the upper jaw are actually special incisors; the real canines lie further back and are quite small. The rest of the teeth are sharply pointed, just the thing for chomping up tough beetles. There are 36 teeth altogether, but fewer in babies. Hedgehogs, like humans, have milk teeth when they are young; the last of these is usually lost at an age of three or four months and the adult dentition is complete well before the animal's first birthday. Eating gritty food such as worms blunts the teeth and in old animals they tend to be quite worn. However, it is very unusual to find a hedgehog with teeth that are worn-out. Presumably, once they reach that stage, they cannot feed properly and soon die.

The hedgehog's soft innards need not concern us. Suffice to say that there is over a metre of guts, plus a very large stomach, plenty of room to stow away a generous helping of dogfood or slugs. The hedgehog seems to have strong digestive juices, which help to cope with a very varied diet, but this does mean that dead hedgehogs decay quickly and soon begin to pong as they effectively begin to digest their own tissues.

## Do hedgehogs bite?

Yes, they do bite, but it's nothing to get in a stew about. In fact it is such a rare event as to be of considerable interest. Of all the many hundreds of hedgehogs I have handled only five have ever bitten me. Two of these were other people's 'tame' hedgehogs who happened to take a particular dislike to me, and one (Emily) always tried to bite me whenever she got the chance. She never bit anyone else, just me, and on one occasion did so as I recorded a TV programme about how nice hedgehogs are. The film shows me chatting away while Emily savaged my finger with considerable determination! This incident demonstrates not only composure on my part, but also that the hedgehog's bite is really not a serious matter.

Each time a hedgehog has bitten me, it has done so slowly and with great deliberation, allowing plenty of time for me to avoid trouble if I wished. Moreover, the long, weak jaws and peculiar gap in the hedgehog's front teeth (see previous page) meant that blood was never drawn, even when I was bitten in some soft spot like the skin between my fingers. Only a few tooth marks remained, even after half a minute's assault. The prickles are more uncomfortable than the teeth. It's not like being bitten by a rat, weasel or squirrel, or example. They are the professionals. They bite fast, hard and deep and are really quite nasty. By comparison the hedgehog is a feeble, amateur biter.

### The rolling-up mechanism

Rolling up into a defensive ball is a very characteristic piece of hedgehog behaviour. No other mammal does it so completely or so effectively. The action is brought about by the contraction of special muscles in the skin. Firstly, a pair of muscles pull the skin forward over the head; another pair pull it backwards over the animal's bottom. Then a big circular muscle operates like the drawstring of a duffel bag. It runs round the animal's body at the edge of the spiny part of the skin (which is very baggy and extra voluminous). As it contracts, it draws the spiny skin downwards and tightly closes it;

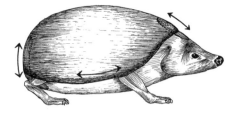

*Rolling-up muscles: thick muscles under the skin help a hedgehog roll up into a tight ball.*

forcing legs, head and tail inside. The result is a tightly contracted ball, completely enveloped in the spiny skin. The head is tucked up against the tail; there is no way in. A hedgehog can stay like this tirelessly for hours; contracting a bit tighter when danger is imminent. As a further defence, tiny skin muscles are attached to the ball-like ends of all the individual spines. When they contract too, the spines are made to bristle and point rigidly in all directions like a mass of barbed wire. In this state hedgehogs are so well protected that they probably have fewer natural enemies than any other mammal of this size (see p. 162).

However, it is comparatively unusual for a hedgehog to roll up completely into a ball. They do it if attacked; some do it if they are picked up, but their usual reaction to threat is merely to hunch themselves up, tuck the head in and move the skin forwards with spines bristling to protect the face. Only when the animal is picked up or bowled over will it go to the next stage of pulling in its feet and drawing the spiny skin tightly right around itself. Some hedgehogs are surprisingly tolerant (or lazy) and do not adopt this full defensive posture unless it is really necessary. This became tragically obvious when we were investigating what happens to young hedgehogs released into the wild after being cared for in an animal hospital. The hedgehogs were as big as adults and very fit, but 3 out of 12 were killed and eaten by a badger during the nine-week study. These hedgehogs had become so tame in captivity that they rarely bothered to roll up when we recaptured them each night for weighing. We meant them no harm of course, so it didn't matter, but they were not to know the danger when accosted by a black-and-white badger face instead of our leather gloves. Badgers are immensely strong animals and also have long claws. This combination is sufficient to penetrate the defence of all but the biggest hedgehog. As badgers become increasingly common, this will be a greater threat to hedgehogs than in the past.

Unfortunately spines are no defence against modern dangers such as motor traffic and mowing machines. Garden strimmers are a particularly nasty threat and often chop bits off hedgehogs as they sleep in their daytime retreats.

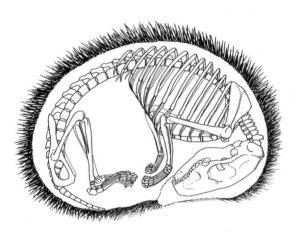

*X-ray view of rolled-up hedgehog*

# Hedgehog senses

We humans depend very much on our eyes for information about our surroundings. Most of our mental pictures are visual ones, so it is hard to imagine life as a hedgehog, for whom vision is comparatively unimportant and smell is the primary sense. Hedgehogs certainly aren't blind; their little black eyes can spot your approach in the dark from a fair distance away. Hedgehogs also learn to recognize major landmarks like trees and houses. Probably these register as distinctive shapes silhouetted against the sky. With eyes so close to the ground, practically everything will be seen that way. The mechanism of the hedgehog's eye is such that it can see things in front of its nose, but probably not in much detail, and certainly not in full colour. The hedgehog's view of the world is probably like that of an old box camera: limited in scope and portrayed in shades of brown and cream. In daylight the eyes work a little better and are capable of distinguishing some colours, but of course they are rarely given the chance because hedgehogs are nocturnal. Under normal circumstances, the hedgehog relies heavily on its nose to find things and probably gets out of the habit of using its eyes very much. Consequently its behaviour sometimes looks to us very short-sighted and stupid as it

walks past juicy food or towards potential danger without apparently noticing what it is doing.

Smell is all important. It is by smell that a hedgehog mainly finds its food, recognizes other hedgehogs and senses the presence of danger (it can detect a person many yards away if the wind is in the right direction). Everywhere it goes, the hedgehog is constantly sniffing the ground or pointing its nose skyward to test the air. Food can be detected, even under more than an inch (3 cm) of soil. The 'smell centres' in the hedgehog's brain are large, indicating their importance. It is quite likely that the hedgehog's nose plays a major role in its social life, helping to recognize other hedgehogs and to distinguish sex and social status, even at a distance, in a way that we do with our eyes.

Many other nocturnal animals have long sensitive whiskers, but although the hedgehog does have a few of these sensory hairs on its snout, they are neither big nor important in its life. Ears are another matter. Though small (only about ½"/1 cm long) and barely poking out of the fur, they are very sensitive. They play an important role in detecting prey; to a hedgehog even worms are probably quite noisy things as they move about. The hedgehog can detect a wide range of sounds and its ability to hear high-pitched notes is probably similar to our own. It is particularly sensitive to abrupt sounds like clicks; a handclap will make it flinch instantly, and the sound of a camera shutter is usually sufficient to cause a sharp ducking of the head and bristling of the spines, blurring the photograph.

## The tale of No. 28

No. 28 was one of the hedgehogs we radio tracked in our garden study (see p. 116). He was almost blind. He showed no reaction to torchlight, frequently ran over our feet and often bumped into things. When he visited a particular food bowl, he sometimes fell off the patio where it was placed. He usually entered and left the garden by the gate, but if this was closed he would crash full tilt into it before turning to one side and using a route under the fence. Of all the hedgehogs we studied, he would surely have been the most likely one to become dependent on food put out by kindly people and surely he, more than any other hedgehog, might have been expected to live as near a food bowl as he could. In fact he travelled considerable distances (at least 1.2 miles/2 km a night) often at very high speed. He often ran so fast his legs were an almost invisible blur and we could hardly keep up with him. He 'courted' female hedgehogs frequently and with vigour. He fought off another that sought to share his food bowl. In short, he managed to be a very competent hedgehog in spite of his disability. No. 28 is a reminder that hedgehogs are not like miniature humans and they live a different sort of life in which eyes and vision are comparatively unimportant.

## Can hedgehogs taste?

They certainly can, yet to our way of thinking they don't seem very discriminating. For example they will eat badly decomposing meat, but perhaps that's only the equivalent of our eating smelly cheese. Some pet hedgehogs become very fussy, causing considerable problems for their owners, refusing to eat anything other than tasty (and very expensive!) mealworms, for example. They will also eat millipedes and certain beetles that exude a nasty chemical to protect themselves from just such a fate. A visiting American scientist once borrowed a hedgehog from me for a week in order to study the way that millipedes avoid being eaten by predators by secreting nasty chemicals. The idea was to offer various species of prey and see which ones the hedgehog rejected. In fact it ate them all! The poor man had read the right books, but the hedgehog had not. He spent much of his precious time in Britain searching for enough millipedes to feed my hedgehog, which finally escaped from its box and made a big mess of his room. I never heard from him again, but I expect he studies something else by now.

*Hedgehog and ground beetle*

## The hedgehog's voice

Normally hedgehogs are silent except for gentle twittering and snuffling as they poke about seeking food. Louder snorting accompanies their courtship rigmarole (p. 79). However, on rare occasions, the hedgehog can let loose the most awful noise. It sounds like a very loud pig squeal. I have heard it only twice; both times when the animal was apprehensive about being handled, although I wasn't actually hurting it. The scream was certainly most alarming and might occasionally serve to put off a would-be predator. Young hedgehogs sometimes make squeaky noises and I have heard a juvenile (barely old enough to have left the nest) make a series of very loud, bird-like chirp-chirp-chirp noises. Again this seems to be unusual. It has also been reported that male East African hedgehogs emit a little 'song' of twittering noises during courtship, but nobody has recorded this behaviour in British hedgehogs.

# Are hedgehogs intelligent?

Basically the answer to this question has to be 'no', although it does depend on what we mean by 'intelligent'. Certainly hedgehogs do not have powers of reasoning and cannot be expected to solve problems of the kind that chimpanzees can sort out. If a hedgehog does overcome a particularly difficult set of circumstances, it probably is the result of chance or trial and error. The solution is unlikely to be remembered and used again.

On the other hand, pet hedgehogs can be taught very simple tasks such as choosing between a black and a white trapdoor, if food is always placed behind one but not the other. Similarly they will learn to distinguish between shapes and symbols; but only to a limited extent. Some hedgehogs will also learn to come when their names are gently called. Few attempts have been made to train hedgehogs more fully than this and there are no reports that suggest that their abilities are any greater than those of rats.

It is certainly true that hedgehogs are individually very variable in their behaviour and personality. This is probably an important aspect of their social behaviour in the wild. In captivity it is noticeable that some hedgehogs are tame from the start, whilst others never even uncurl without signs of acute nervousness. Some captive hedgehogs are similar to dogs and cats in that they will behave in a relaxed way with their normal keeper, but never settle down with anyone else. Even hedgehogs in the same litter grow up with different personalities.

There are plenty of stories which show that hedgehogs have reasonably good memories, especially for places. For example, one animal that was used to living indoors, always sleeping in one place and always being fed near the kitchen stove, was sent to live elsewhere for several months. On her return she immediately behaved as though she had never been away, and knew exactly where to find her nest box and food.

It is interesting that memory survives hibernation. During winter the brain is almost completely shut down and inactive (unlike our own brain during normal sleep), yet whatever mechanism enables memories to be stored is not wrecked by the drastic changes in temperature and activity.

## Simple tricks to try and teach to a hedgehog

1 . Pulling food into the cage. Put piece of favourite food on a flat plastic strip (e.g. a ruler or tape). Start with this adjacent to the bars, so that the animal learns to nibble food outside its cage. Then place it further away, forcing the hedgehog to learn to pull the strip towards the cage before it can have its reward. If it gets the hang of this problem, gradually lengthen the strip to see how far away the animal is able to recognize food and how hard it is willing to work in order to get it. Some birds will learn a similar trick very quickly and a hedgehog has learnt to pull in food from 12"(30cm) away.

2. Keep a hedgehog in a large box or pen. Construct a barrier with two sliding or hanging doors in it. This should span the width of the pen and be too tall for the hedgehog to climb over (i.e. 1 foot/ 30cm high). Beyond the doors the pen should be divided down the middle with wire mesh to form two parallel corridors, food being available at the end of only one. Colour the two doors differently and always

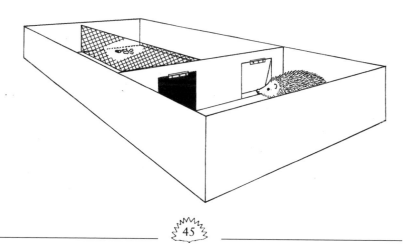

put food behind the same colour door. When the hedgehog has got used to always going through (say) the left hand black door instead of the right hand white door, swap the doors over. Does it still go to the left door or to the black door? Repeat the experiment using doors of the same colour to see if your hedgehog can tell right from left. Use the coloured doors, swapping them randomly from left to right (but always have the food behind the same colour) to see if it's the colour the hedgehog recognizes, not the side. Make sure the food is at the far end of the corridor and not so near the door that the animal can smell which door it is behind.

# Parasites: fleas and ticks

The hedgehog has a well deserved reputation for being flea-ridden. It is very unusual to find one with no fleas on it and sometimes there may be up to 500 on a single animal. What makes this appear even worse is the fact that the coarse hair and widely spaced spines do nothing to hide the fleas from our horrified gaze. The fleas seem all the more numerous because they are so conspicuous and constantly on the move. Even when there are only a few fleas present, as is normal, the hedgehog still appears to be over-endowed with 'little friends'. Fleas can jump over 100 times their own height (equivalent to a man jumping over London's Telecom Tower!); but most of the time they scurry about in a frantic, hurried manner among the hedgehog's belly and facial hairs. To help in its rapid movement through this hairy jungle, the flea's body is very narrow and also very smooth and shiny.

Just because hedgehogs often have lots of fleas and these are very conspicuous, it doesn't mean that hedgehogs are the source of all fleas. Their reputation in that respect is wholly undeserved. People often say, 'Oh, my dog's got fleas again. He must have found a hedgehog.' This is a wickedly unjust accusation. If your dog has fleas, then it probably got them from another dog (or perhaps some other mammal). It isn't fair to blame the hedgehog. The only way to be even half certain of where the fleas have come from is to get them identified by an expert. The point is that in Britain we have over 50 different kinds of fleas, half of them only found on bats and birds. Many of the others are 'host specific', that is to say they live on only one type

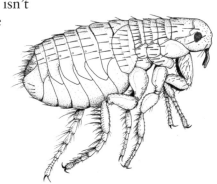

*Hedgehog flea (magnified 20 times)*

of animal and very rarely on any other species. The hedgehog flea (scientifically known as *Archaeopsylla erinacei*) is one of these. It lives on hedgehogs, sometimes on foxes and only very occasionally on other things. It is easy to understand why. The hedgehog's skin is a peculiar micro-habitat. The fleas are accustomed to the bare skin, draughty spaces between the spines, and harsh fur. If they find themselves in the dense, warm, fluffy coat of a cat or dog, they must immediately know that they are in the wrong habitat. It would be just like taking a grouse from the open moors and putting it in a dense thicket of trees – very upsetting! Consequently, hedgehog fleas do not remain on wrong hosts, but drop off and hope to find another hedgehog. The same goes for hedgehog fleas that get on to humans. They will do this (especially if made to jump or if they are leaving the body of a fresh-dead hedgehog) and they will bite; but they do not stay long before leaving to find a proper host.

The reverse is also true; the hedgehog's skin is such a peculiar environment that fleas from other species don't like to live there. Consequently you very rarely find any other types of flea on the hedgehog. I have collected over 2,000 fleas from hedgehogs and only one of them was not the special hedgehog flea (it was a mole flea, *Hystrichopsylla talpae*).

Fleas feed by sucking blood and sometimes, for reasons that are not fully understood, their digestive system goes haywire causing them to excrete blood as a brown, gooey mess on the hedgehog's spines. This leads to a curious condition seen in the summer when some hedgehogs seem to have lots of blood on their spines but no obvious wounds from which it could have come.

### Getting rid of fleas

If you want to get rid of the fleas, when keeping a captive hedgehog for example, it is easily done using the commercially available flea powders sold by pet shops. The powder should be lightly dusted among the hedgehog's spines, taking care to avoid the animal's eyes. Naturally it is difficult to get the powder on to the hedgehog's belly when it is rolled up, but there is no need to try too hard. Powder will shake off in the nest and bedding, soon killing the remaining fleas as the hedgehog moves about.

In the wild, fleas breed in the nest, not on the body of their host. Baby flea larvae grow up in the nest lining, so if you are keeping a pet hedgehog for a while, it is a good idea to change the animal's bedding occasionally to get rid of these lodgers.

People often worry that depriving a hedgehog of its fleas might be harmful in some way, but why should it? Would you mind? In fact, as hedgehogs appear completely indifferent to the presence of their fleas (even lots of them), it is hardly likely that they will be unduly bothered by their absence.

Hedgehogs in New Zealand have no fleas, having lost them somewhere on their journey downunder.

# A nasty problem

One of the nastiest and most upsetting experiences is to find a hedgehog with small maggots in its skin, especially around the eyes. This looks particularly horrible and, sadly, is not uncommonly seen in sickly baby hedgehogs especially in late summer.

What seems to happen is that the hedgehog becomes ill and lethargic, its body temperature falls and flies mistake it for dead and lay their eggs (these little white things are sometimes found in the fur and should be swabbed with dilute disinfectant and combed out). The eggs may hatch before the hedgehog is actually dead and lead to the distressing sight of a maggoty animal. It is probably kindest to kill the hedgehog, especially if its eyes are affected, even though it will not itself show any signs of concern for its plight. By careful cleaning with disinfectant the situation may be retrieved, but the hedgehog is likely to die anyway from other causes. It may not, but the omens aren't good.

# Ticks and their removal

Ticks are distant relatives of spiders. The adult form has a shiny grey globular body, almost about ½"(1cm) long. It has eight tiny legs at the front end and a set of mouth parts which dig into the hedgehog's skin to suck blood. These rather nasty animals can be made to let go and drop off by touching their back end with a burning cigarette. They can also be tweaked off with forceps, but this needs practice or you leave the mouthparts stuck in the hedgehog's skin. To avoid such a mishap leading to a septic wound, the skin should be swabbed with alcohol or disinfectant. Sometimes dousing with disinfectant alone will make the ticks let go. Smearing the ticks with margarine, olive oil or washing-up liquid blocks their breathing holes. They then suffocate and drop off. Left alone, the ticks will feed on the animals hedgehog's blood for a while then drop off of their own accord, but it is best to kill them if you can to avoid their getting on to pets. One hedgehog may have several ticks on its body, but most have none. Sometimes young larval ticks may be found; small, flat, orange-brown things. Unlike fleas, these do not jump.

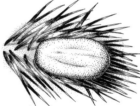

*Tick among spines*

*Adult tick*

# In sickness and in health

Hedgehogs suffer from a long list of ailments, to which may be added the injuries caused by accidents. Certainly increasing numbers are now taken into care at animal rescue centres, and many people want to do their best for the sick and injured hedgehogs that they may find. The best advice is to seek specialist help, either via a local vet, the RSPCA or the British Hedgehog Preservation Society (see p. 203). Looking after hedgehogs is messy and time consuming; better to use the experience of others rather than cause suffering and distress either to yourself or your sick hedgehog. Nevertheless, it may be helpful to provide some notes and suggestions here.

Sick hogs are often cold and are best kept warm by keeping them on a hot water bottle wrapped in a blanket to disperse the heat. They should not be warmed by an overhead lamp shining down. Often warmth is enough to make them perk up and feed. They should have plenty to drink, and a vet may inject some physiologically balanced solution to top up their blood stream. Obvious injuries can be cleaned up with warm water and disinfectants, perhaps diluted, as one might treat a child with cuts. Unfortunately, a hedgehog's natural response to being examined is to roll up. This makes life difficult and may also cause severe pain in the case of certain types of injury – all the more reason for seeking trained assistance.

Wheezing and gurgling are often signs of severe lungworm infection, and sloppy droppings may suggest poisoning. Running in circles may indicate a bacterial infection. Maggots and fly eggs are easily treated, but broken bones are best left to the vet. Large patches of missing spines (perhaps caused by a strimmer or mower), and even

quite severe skin wounds will heal up naturally if the animal is kept clean and dry. More detailed advice is available in Kay Bullen's book *Hedgehog Rehabilitation* (see list on p. 202). Generally speaking, the kind of treatments that one might use on a child or a dog will probably not do a hedgehog much harm. However, it has been suggested that homeopathic medicines might be a more natural form of cure. The problem here is the lack of scientific validation. Sick hedgehogs may well get better after homeopathic treatments, but they might have got better anyway. Without properly structured scientific experiments it's hard to know whether such treatment actually does any good or not, although it can't do much harm apart from depriving the animal of some more conventional and proven medicines such as antibiotics. Unfortunately, the hedgehogs cannot express an opinion for themselves.

## Hedgehog ailments

Comparatively few detailed post mortem examinations have been carried out, so there is often doubt about exactly what may have been wrong with them (typical is the assumption that a dead hedgehog in the garden has been poisoned by the neighbour's use of slug pellets for example). Unfortunately, we don't know the relative importance of different causes of death, but a study by some vets in 1991 reported post mortem details of 74 dead hedgehogs (nearly half of which were killed on the roads). The animals were all examined for parasites and poison residues. At least 31 were affected by more than one of these, so the final cause of death was not always clear. There were fleas on 22 animals (no surprise there), ticks on 11 and mange mites on one. These external parasites are relatively harmless, but many had intestinal worms and some harboured organisms that can infect humans.

There is usually a significant prevalence of lungworms among dead hedgehogs. They cause a type of pneumonia that is sometimes fatal. Lungworms are a special kind of nematode worm and are often very widespread. They are very tiny (invisible without a microscope), but they attack the lungs in large numbers. This causes the hedgehog to produce a lot of watery fluid in its air passages and breathing becomes laboured. The animal wheezes and coughs as though it smoked forty cigarettes a day. Lungworm is also a problem in sheep and dogs and the same medicine used for these can also help cure hedgehogs, but this is best done with the help of a vet. Hedgehogs get these parasites as a result of eating worms and slugs within which the parasite larvae are living. Adults are more often infected than juveniles because these parasites come from eating infected prey and so it takes time to acquire them. It's perfectly natural and hard to avoid. Sometimes infestations may be sufficiently severe as to result in death, but normally a hedgehog carries relatively few of these parasites and the only evidence is their microscopic eggs in the hedgehog's droppings. Not many people spend their time looking at droppings that closely, so their presence escapes notice.

# Hogs in hospital

Nigel Reeve analysed data collected by Dru Burdon in Jersey, to establish what ailments the animals most commonly suffered from and what success the Jersey rehabilitators had in restoring their sick hedgehogs to a healthy life. There were 3,177 admissions in 9 years (1995-2005), equivalent to 4% of the total hedgehog population of Jersey. Two thirds of them were treated and released, 30% died and the rest were 'kept in'. About 50% of the intake were suffering from natural problems such as parasites, the rest were injured, poisoned or orphaned. Over half of the orphans survived and were released. The lungworms *Crenosoma* and *Capillaria* were particularly common and 48% of the animals examined were infected by one or both types. There were only

a few tapeworm infections. Released animals were ear tagged and 185 animals were found again, with nearly half having survived more than one year, many being seen more than once and one animal lived more than 5 years after release.

# Hedgehogs as disease carriers

Hedgehogs are host to a number of viruses, bacteria and microscopic organisms which may cause serious illness in themselves or to other animals. For example, the kidneys may contain leptospires, tiny bacteria which are distributed in the urine and may cause sickness and fevers. The intestine may contain *Salmonella*, the bacterium which causes food poisoning.

Among these was a case of *Salmonella typhimurium*. This is the bacterium that causes food poisoning and became famous in the 1960s by developing resistance to antibiotics. The related *S. enteritidis* was found in no less than 13 (18.9%) of the 74 hedgehogs, 10 of them from gardens. This was the 'bug' that caused trouble a few years ago with food poisoning in eggs and dairy products. There was a huge fuss on TV and in many press stories which also resulted in a ministerial resignation and lots of bankrupt farmers. This reminds us that hedgehogs are not just cute creatures, they are also potential carriers of disease. They and their faeces might well cause the spread of food poisoning among humans, pets and farm animals. It is important to maintain good hygienic standards when handling them. It is also important to keep sick animals separately lest they infect others.

To make a list of all these potential nasties would make the hedgehog seem like a disease time-bomb, a threat to public health. However, this should be seen in perspective; most of these things have been found in other mammals at some time or other and the hedgehog is no more of a danger than any other animal.

The good news is that the hedgehog is actually less of a threat than some animals. It does not appear to be an important carrier of rabies, for example, unlike the fox. It has probably played no significant role in spreading that disease across Europe in recent years and if rabies ever broke out in Britain, the hedgehog should not become a serious danger to us.

Something else we can be glad about is the fact that hedgehogs have not been identified as major co-villains with the badger in the spread of tuberculosis among cattle. This disease has become a serious problem in the past 20 years (mostly in the south and west of England) and the campaign to kill badgers as a means of solving the problem resulted in a lot of controversy. Hedgehogs do not appear to be important carriers of TB, although very few have actually been tested to make sure. On the other hand, hedgehogs can carry foot-and-mouth disease. In the event of an outbreak, it is easy to

*Hedgehog with ringworm*

see that hedgehogs could carry this disease from one herd to another in their nocturnal rambles, despite conventional quarantine precautions. One interesting aspect of this is that experiments have demonstrated that if a foot-and-mouth infected hedgehog goes into hibernation, it will still be infective when it resumes activity the following year. Thus the hedgehog could act as a dangerous over-wintering reservoir of the disease. However, so long as foot-and-mouth is kept out of Britain, the hedgehog will not earn any black marks here.

One minor disease that I have studied in some detail is hedgehog ringworm. Ringworm is actually caused by a fungus, a bit like athlete's foot. There are several different types and they are found on the skin of various wild and domestic mammals. Occasionally humans become infected (it causes an itchy inflammation) but it's easily cured. The interesting thing is that hedgehogs have their own special kind of ringworm. It seems to do no harm, although in chronic infections the hedgehog's ears may become swollen and crusty-looking (though evidently not itchy). Hedgehog ringworm was first identified among New Zealand hedgehogs and later shown to occur in Britain. With the help of Mary English at Bristol Royal Infirmary, I sampled a large number of hedgehogs (mostly road casualties) and found that one in five carried the fungus in its skin and hair roots. Males were much more often infected than females, and ringworm was found more often on the head than on the rest of the body. Both observations are probably explained by the fact that males fight by head-butting each other, probably jabbing infective material into their opponent's skin. Urban hedgehogs were more likely to carry ringworm than those in rural areas. Our experimental efforts to transmit the fungus from one animal to another were a failure and even where it was already established, the fungus seemed to develop slowly and cause the hedgehog no harm. Hedgehog ringworm can be transmitted to humans, but it seems to be such an inefficient parasite that this rarely happens. I have never taken any precautions to avoid it (save for washing my hands after working with hedgehogs) and the fungus hasn't got to me yet. It is possible that children or others with more tender skin might become infected, but not very likely.

As a disease carrier, the hedgehog does not seem to be a serious cause for concern. It comes a long way behind rats, mice and foxes as a disease threat. This fairly rosy view needs to be qualified by adding that, as usual, few detailed studies have been made of the hedgehog in this connection, so we can't be really certain of the facts. And if some hedgehog-borne disease ever did break out, our lack of basic knowledge of this species could suddenly become a disaster.

# Strange behaviour: self-anointing and other funny goings-on

One of the most extraordinary activities that a hedgehog performs has been christened 'self-anointing'. A hedgehog will suddenly abandon normal behaviour and begin to produce large quantities of frothy saliva. Then, with great smacking of the lips, it will proceed to use its tongue to flick this white foam over its back and flank. To reach the more difficult places, like the middle of the back, a hedgehog will twist and contort itself into a grotesque shape, protruding its tongue to a quite extraordinary degree. Sometimes this self-anointing will only last a minute or two, but occasionally the hedgehog will become almost obsessively engrossed, ignore all else and carry on for up to an hour. Then it suddenly stops and resumes normal activity. Self-anointing is not confined to European hedgehogs, it has been reported from other species too.

*Chewing leather often sets them off.*

It is a quite extraordinary performance, which leaves the animal flecked with foam, just like streaks of soap suds. It is not at all clear what starts the whole business off. Often it begins when the animal smells or chews something aromatic like furniture varnish, dog faeces, a cigarette end or a cigar butt. Briefly chewing shoe leather often gets pet hedgehogs going. In the wild, hedgehogs do not necessarily encounter these stimulants, but may be triggered by other things. However, the presence of a special chemical substance is not essential, sometimes even distilled water is enough to set them off. Yet many hedgehogs, perhaps the majority, never seem to self-anoint at all. It's all very puzzling.

A big study in Belgium recorded signs of recent anointing in only 2% of hedgehogs encountered, suggesting that it is not a common occurrence (the figure increased to 11% when evidence of dried saliva was counted, but this might have included muck on spines from other sources). That study also showed males (young and old) self-anointing twice as often as females, and young animals did it more often than adults.

Theories have been advanced to explain this energetic and messy behaviour, most of them not very plausible. One suggestion was that the saliva might camouflage the hedgehog's own odour and thus hide it from predators, but surely a predator would then simply learn to recognise the smell of the saliva and attack the victim anyway? The idea that it was a method of getting rid of fleas doesn't seem correct either – or if it is, it doesn't work. It is certainly not performed more often by flea-ridden animals and in fact is often observed among pet hedgehogs that are kept scrupulously clean by their owners.

Another suggestion was that self-anointing was stimulated by chewing toad skin (true) and that this contains poisonous substances (also true). The result would then be to distribute the toad skin poison in the hedgehog's frothy saliva all over the latter's spines. This would arm each spine with a poison tip, greatly increasing its defensive value. While this theory may be plausible (and its author provided experimental evidence by jabbing his own skin with clean and with 'poisoned' spines to study the comparative effect!), it cannot be the full explanation for self-anointing. For a start, hedgehogs do not need toad skin, but will self-anoint after contact even with innocuous substances. Moreover, the hedgehog's spines are a very effective protection anyway; they don't need poisoned tips.

I think self-anointing may be connected with scent. Suppose that the saliva contained a pheromone, a smelly substance recognized by other hedgehogs. (This is quite possible: male pigs have scent in their saliva.) Spreading the froth over the body would allow the spines and fur to act like an 'air wick' and disseminate scent on the air (moths have special feathery structures that perform this function). This way, a hedgehog could advertise its presence to others of its own species and perhaps thereby defend its immediate surroundings or attract a mate, and young ones could be more easily traced by their mother. The spiny skin would be adequate defence against any predators that might also be attracted. Such an idea fits in well with what we know about hedgehog social behaviour.

This is obviously an area deserving more research. All we can say for certain is that self-anointing is such an elaborate and energetic performance that it must serve some purpose; we just don't know what.

## Running in circles

Another strange piece of reported hedgehog behaviour is the habit of running in circles. This should not be confused with the usual snorting, circling waltz performed by pairs of courting hedgehogs, shuffling around each other. Running in circles is just that, running, following

a circular track 10 or 15 yards in diameter. It is performed by a single hedgehog, all on its own, scooting round and round without evident boredom or self-consciousness for lap after lap. This may go on for an hour or more, sometimes on successive nights.

Some say it's a sign of frustration. If so then you'd expect captive hedgehogs to do it a lot of the time. The jokers say that hedgehogs run in circles because their left legs are shorter than the other two.

Such frenetic behaviour is surely not normal nor likely to be connected with any aspect of the hedgehog's customary stoical habits. Could this be some kind of abnormal behaviour brought about by illness? An infection in the ear, for example, could upset the sense of balance and stop the hedgehog from walking straight, like being drunk. But drunks don't run, nor do they go in endless repeated circles. Still, illness could be the clue. It may be significant that running in circles seems to have been first reported in the 1960s and frequently observed since then. It is not mentioned in earlier books on hedgehogs, despite extensive reviews of other habits. Did the earlier writers simply fail to observe this distinctive, conspicuous and enigmatic activity or is it something that hedgehogs have only started to do recently? The 1960s and 1970s were a period when large quantities of increasingly diverse chemicals were manufactured for use against garden pests. These substances are supposedly 'safe', but they are only tested on a limited range of animals (not including hedgehogs). It is known that certain chemicals may affect one species but not another. Could running in circles be a symptom of some kind of poisoning? Let's hope not and that it's just another bit of mysterious hedgehog behaviour in need of investigation. An ear infection on one side only seems the most likely explanation.

# The hedgehog's menu:
# the natural diet

Nowadays many hedgehogs must get a lot of their food off plates in people's gardens (feeding garden hedgehogs is discussed further on p. 115 and feeding them in captivity is described on p. 92). However, their normal method of feeding is to quarter the ground meticulously, poking their noses into tussocks and crannies, seeking anything edible. Damp, grazed grassland is probably one of the best hunting grounds and hedgehogs may travel some distance to a good feeding place.

In the dark it is difficult to see what a hedgehog eats, although eager crunching noises suggest when a beetle is being devoured, while slobbery lip-smacking is more indicative of earthworms and slugs. Close inspection of the finger-sized black droppings, so often left on our lawns, shows glistening bits of beetles to be particularly frequent prey items, but more details can be gleaned from studying stomach contents. So I sent a box of hedgehog stomachs to one of my friends, Dr Derek Yalden of Manchester University. He's still one of my friends in spite of that. Moreover, he was able to list all the identifiable items found in 137 hedgehog stomachs collected from animals killed by gamekeepers or run over on the road. Beetles, such as cockchafers, weevils and dung beetles, were found in three quarters of the stomachs; testimony to the importance of these as hedgehog food. Over half the stomachs contained earwigs; caterpillars and slugs were also very frequent prey. Sometimes quite large numbers had been eaten by one animal in a very short time: 63 caterpillars in one case, 22 earwigs in another and 75 beetles in another. These creatures would be at the very top of every gardener's 'hit list', so it's obvious that hedgehogs must do a lot of good in gardens and farmland. It is likely that each hedgehog kills at least a hundred such invertebrates, many of them pests, in a night's foraging and thousands every year. Earthworms are

*Hedgehog dropping*

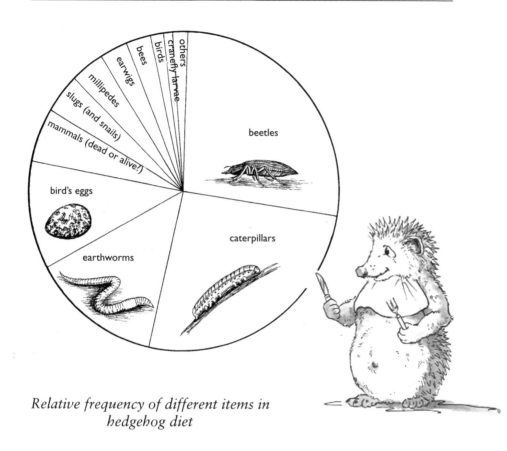

*Relative frequency of different items in hedgehog diet*

often taken of course; but, more surprisingly, so are large numbers of millipedes. These creatures produce nasty-tasting chemicals which are meant to deter predators from eating them. Certainly shrews eat few millipedes, but hedgehogs gobble them with relish, along with supposedly 'distasteful' ground beetles. It's not that hedgehogs have no sense of taste; simply that they are not put off by the chemical defences of these invertebrates. It may even be that these very same chemicals taste and smell so strongly as to actually help the hedgehog find the creatures that produce them: a counter-productive defence.

In short, it seems that hedgehogs will eat anything edible that they can find, but there are some notable exceptions to this. They seem to eat very few snails, presumably because their jaws are not able to cope with the shells. Hedgehogs also rarely eat centipedes, probably because these can bite and they can run fast too. Grasshoppers, despite their abundance, contribute little to the hedgehog's fare; again probably because they can leap away and are too fast to catch. Mice and voles are probably eaten quite often, especially nestlings. Adults too may be consumed either as carrion or caught alive when cornered in a confined space (e.g. under a shed). Shrews and moles are eaten, even though these have distasteful skin glands. Nine of Derek Yalden's hedgehogs had eaten bits of rabbit, probably found lying about as carrion. However, there have been astonishing tales told of hedgehogs actually chasing baby rabbits, rats and chickens and even killing them. This is hard to believe, partly because hedgehogs don't run fast enough and partly because their jaws and teeth are not suited to big-time carnivory. Nevertheless baby rabbits are pretty silly and if a hedgehog did once manage to grab hold of an unwary one, it could hang on or perhaps roll up around its victim and spike it on its spines.

The biggest mystery must surely be that hedgehogs seem to eat very few woodlice. This is odd because woodlice are very common creatures, especially in gardens. They can't be too distasteful to eat

because shrews often take them. Nor is it that they are too small because hedgehogs often eat tiny bugs and daddy longlegs that have far less meat on them than woodlice. It may be that woodlice are too difficult to pick up in the hedgehog's teeth. A few simple observations ought to clarify that point.

Bits of grass and the odd leaf are often swallowed along with worms and other prey. Hedgehogs will also eat squashy fruit and of course bread and milk (see p. 121), but their main diet consists of animal material. Mostly this comprises the invertebrates mentioned above, but also vertebrates such as lizards and the occasional frog. Certainly a more predaceous side to the hedgehog's character is revealed when the chicks of ground-nesting birds are encountered. Chicks are eagerly attacked and eaten, in a gruesome manner too. Gulls, terns, gamebirds and doubtless pipits and skylarks, must all lose a few broods to hedgehogs from time to time. Eggs are also eaten, usually leaving a mess of broken shells, stomped into a mixture of yolk and nest lining. The chart on p. 63 suggests that eggs are often found in the hedgehog's diet. In fact of course they will be infrequent outside the breeding season. Moreover, their importance is exaggerated in my digram because many of the hedgehogs used in that study came from gamekeepers who had baited their traps with eggs. Nevertheless, it is precisely because of such depredations that gamekeepers regard the hedgehog as an enemy, but whenever careful studies have been made it has become clear that hedgehogs are insignificant predators. They may account for two or three per cent of clutches lost, one tenth of the numbers taken by foxes, and really not enough to warrant all the fuss made by gamekeepers (see p. 152). One study of partridge nests found that hedgehogs destroyed far fewer than were lost due to careless workers using farm machinery.

## Hedgehogs, tins and drink containers

It was once reported that hedgehogs had discovered that civil servants discarded large numbers of disposable plastic tea and coffee cups around the grounds of a government research station. The cups contained lovely sweet and creamy dregs well worth poking your head in as far as possible to lick up. But once inside, a hedgehog's spines are pressed tight against the walls of the cup, tighter still as it

tries to push further in to lick up the last little bits. Then of course, as the head is withdrawn, the spines jam into the soft polystyrene walls of the cup and the hedgehog is stuck with a plastic cup on its head. Numbers of bemused, helmeted hedgehogs were reported wandering about. A similar unfortunate was reported from Orkney with its head wedged in a plastic yoghurt pot. 'McFlurry' containers, issued by McDonalds food outlets, caused the same sort of problems. The British Hedgehog Preservation Society pressed the company to withdraw them from use, but several years later they were still only experimenting with a new design. So, no hurry for McFlurry! They did urge people not to scatter litter about, but I wonder how many of their customers ever even read messages like that printed on food packets? Pictures of trapped hedgehogs might be more effective.

Given time, a hedgehog might use its front paws to split and rip off most disposable plastic cups, but not tins. Countless tins are opened by picnickers every year and thoughtlessly tossed away. These not only have juicy remains inside, much to a hedgehog's liking, but they also have a rough spiky rim which grip the spines tightly like a collar and stop a hedgehog getting its head out from cans of a certain size. I once saw a large stuffed hedgehog in a museum alongside the open, discarded tin of cream that had been its downfall. The moral of these stories is of course that hedgehogs shouldn't be so greedy and we shouldn't be so careless and untidy with our litter.

# Hedgehogs out and about

When moving about, hedgehogs look uncannily like clockwork toys. This is because the body is surrounded by a fringing 'skirt' of long hair which hides the feet. The animal also walks with its legs bent in such a way that the whole body is low-slung and close to the ground, again concealing the feet. Hedgehogs thus move as though on hidden wheels, without visible signs of propulsion. It then comes as a surprise to discover that hedgehogs can run quite fast. They raise themselves up on straighter legs and make a bee-line for some distant objective, reaching average speeds of 30-40 metres per minute: nearly 2 miles per hour. To us, this is only a fast walking pace, but in the hedgehog it looks and is really rapid. Thirty metres is 150 times the animal's own length. Moreover, some hedgehogs keep up an average speed of this sort for several minutes at a stretch, including short sprints of 2 metres per second (6 mph) or more; about the maximum speed we can walk without breaking into a run. Careful study has shown that the average speed of male hedgehogs in the course of a night's wanderings is nearly twice the average speed of females.

Despite these occasional bursts of athleticism, the hedgehog's normal gait is a patient, unflappable trundle. Again, this gives the misleading impression that the hedgehog is unlikely to dig, climb or do anything else dramatic. They certainly can dig, but don't usually bother except to escape by excavating a scrape under a fence or some other obstacle. They can climb too, although it's not clear why they bother. Hedgehogs have been found in upstairs bedrooms, having arrived, Errol Flynn-style, up the ivy clad wall and in through the open window. Almost as unbelievable, I have now been told by seven different

*Errol hog*

people about hedgehogs climbing to their bedrooms via the stairs. Climbing stairs is strange enough (and quite difficult), but I really can't see why a hedgehog would want to bother. What does it think it's doing, what does it think it will find? At least one hedgehog has been found hibernating in a thatched roof and I was once told about another house where the attic was opened up for the first time in 20 years and there were two dead hedgehogs inside. There are also stories of hedgehogs reaching roof gutters by squeezing up the inside of drainpipes. They will, in mountaineering spirit, 'chimney' up a house, bracing themselves in the gap between a down pipe and the angle of a wall. Mere wire fences are a doddle and even wooden slatted fences over a metre high (4ft) will be scaled on occasions.

Hedgehogs can also squeeze through extraordinarily small holes. They seem to be such podgy animals that they could never negotiate a gap less than 3"(10 cm) wide. It's easy to forget that much of the hedgehog's apparent bulk is in its loose-fitting skin. This is like a chunky sweater: very mobile and enclosing a comparatively slight occupant. With spines laid flat, a hedgehog can get under a shed, through a tiny hole or between the slats of a chestnut paling fence. Once into a small space it can bristle the spines and become impossible to dislodge. A lady once wrote to me saying that a hedgehog had crawled into an old Wellington boot, what should she do? I suggested she wore the other one and hopped, but in all seriousness little else was possible. The only way to get a hedgehog out of such a tight spot is to wait for it to extract itself.

*Hedgehogs can easily squeeze through small gaps.*

These matters were most clearly demonstrated to me when I did my first 'hedgehog' radio interview for the BBC. I put the animal on the floor and concentrated on my questions and diction. Next thing there was no sign of my co-star. It had vanished! BBC studios are not noted for their lavish furnishings or general clutter. It was a square room with fitted carpet and nowhere to hide. It took nearly 20 minutes of searching brief cases, the corridor outside and every inch of the studio before we discovered the animal wedged in the 2"(5 cm) gap between a heavy cupboard and the wall. There was no getting the bristling blighter out, so we had to empty the cupboard and move it before recapturing my hedgehog. Doubtless that performance would have made a more interesting broadcast than whatever it was that I had actually said in the interview.

Hedgehogs can swim fairly well and one was reported to have swum across the Thames at Henley. At least two of my radio-tracked animals have also crossed rivers, and one ended up in a millpond

*Providing a way out from a garden pond may save many lives.*

*Hedgehog swimming with New Zealand scaup*

complex, requiring a risky rescue in the dark. When I was in New Zealand, I found a particularly dusty hedgehog out one evening and decided to put it into a nearby lake to get clean. That way I could also take some photos of it swimming. However, before I could get my camera ready, it set off for the far shore, about half a mile away! It swam out into deep water and began to go round in circles. Soon a small group of astonished ducks gathered around it, staring in disbelief at this unfamiliar aquatic species and in utter amazement as I took my clothes off and swam out to stop it drowning. This animal must have been swimming non-stop for at least ten minutes, probably more, easily enough to cross most rivers. Several radio tracking studies have confirmed that hedgehogs can and do swim across rivers. The fact that they often drown in small garden ponds is due to their inability to climb out (see p. 111).

## Hedgehogs out and about: how far do they travel?

If you try to follow a hedgehog to see where it goes, it isn't long before it disappears under a bush or through a fence. It's not easy to watch furtive movements in the dark anyway. So, although it may be possible to follow a hedgehog for a short time, you are unlikely to learn much about its general movements. The 'experts' have exactly the same problem, which is why so little is known about the nocturnal wanderings of hedgehogs; the practical difficulties are such that few studies have even been attempted. The best way to follow hedgehogs at night is to use 'radio tracking', a technique in which a miniature radio transmitter is attached to the animal so that everywhere it goes it can be traced using a direction-finding radio receiver. All sorts of animals have been radio tracked now, but only relatively few of such studies have been made of British hedgehogs.

These days we often see radio-tracking studies on TV programmes, but when I started, back in the 1960s, the idea of putting radios on hedgehogs was considered highly eccentric. In fact, one of the biggest problems was to convince the Post Office that I was serious, because they had responsibility for issuing radio licences. After six months of discussion, they finally agreed; and so it was that my hedgehogs became licensed as 'Testing and Development Stations' in accordance with the Wireless and Telegraphy Act, 1949. The licence itself ran to several pages of foolscap paper, and I was supposed to keep a log of everything said during transmissions! Nowadays a general licence allows anyone to use a special radio frequency for tracking animals. It's up to the investigators to avoid their signals getting confused with each other. It happens just the same and one of my students reported that a hedgehog he had been following was sending strong signals from up in a tree! It turned out that this was actually a red squirrel carrying a radio in a study by another of my students, using exactly the same radio frequency.

## Bleep bleep – radio hedgehog on the air

My first design of radio transmitter was attached to an elastic harness, tailor-made to fit its carrier. The harness had to be elastic to allow the animal to roll up. Modern designs are smaller and can be glued directly to the spines. The transmitter weighs less than 5% of the hedgehog itself, so it is not a major encumbrance (equivalent to a human carrying an empty rucksack). Power comes from a tiny battery. Radio transmitters can be home-made and the direction-finding aerial is not difficult to make either. Anyone could go radio tracking hedgehogs if it were not for problems with the receiver. The authorities will not allow transmitters to work on radio frequencies that might interfere with the BBC or police walkie-talkies, so hedgehog transmitters must be built to emit a higher frequency signal. In turn that means the receiver must be capable of picking up such signals and normal transistor radios can't. However, you can buy a special converter which allows a normal transistor radio of good quality to be modified to do the job. Thus a make-do, but workable radio-tracking system could be built for about £250, given a bit of patience and workshop expertise. However, such equipment is not easy to use and all our studies now employ specialist transmitters and receivers (supplied by Biotrack of Wareham in Dorset). The former cost over £100 each, the latter about 10-15 times as much. Hedgehog research is not easy to do on the cheap!

My original radio transmitters were home-made and had to have a flexible aerial to allow the animals to roll up. Unfortunately this reduced their efficiency by about 95%, giving them a range of only about 100 metres. Modern equipment allows hedgehogs to be located at distances more than five times greater than this. A special aerial indicates which direction the signal is coming from, allowing us to walk towards the hedgehog until we can see it. Hedgehogs often do nothing at all for hours; so following them can be pretty boring. It can be chilly too, as the frost settles or mist rises around your knees at 4 a.m. Also, wandering about in the dead of night waving around what appears to be a TV aerial is not easily explained to a squad car full of sceptical policemen.

Anyway our radio-tracking studies suggest that male hedgehogs travel about 1-2 miles(2-3 km) a night, at least in grassy areas. Males wander further than females, and both probably travel greater distances where there is less food to delay them. Two and a half miles (4km) is

probably about the furthest straight-line distance a night's wandering would extend to. However, these estimates are based on our studies of hedgehogs living on farmland and a golf course with its adjacent gardens. There is little to stop them wandering freely over wide areas, but elsewhere in thick woodland or built-up areas they appear to travel much less.

The sort of precise radio tracking necessary for studying hedgehogs is very difficult in built-up areas because walls, fences and metal objects distort the signals. Nor is it easy for the observer to move about freely, and almost impossible to avoid annoying the local residents, so despite the abundance of hedgehogs in suburban areas, this is one of the more difficult habitats in which to study them. Yet generalizations about hedgehogs based on studies elsewhere may not be valid in town gardens.

The normal pattern of movement consists of a slow and careful circuitous meandering in search of food, every possible place being investigated. This is then followed by a brisk walk to another likely spot where further searches will be made. Whilst seeking food the hedgehog wanders to left and right and often in circles, so adding considerably to the total distance covered. Most nights, the animal will end up where it started, back at its daytime nest. It will remain there until dusk and then begin another night's foray. However, hedgehogs do not always return to the same nest, especially in summer. They may stay somewhere else for several days, then return to a previously used nest.

Several of our studies have shown that males change their nests more frequently than females, with males using a fresh one almost every day and females staying in the same nest for a week or more. At different times, the same nest may be occupied by a series of different hedgehogs, so it is difficult to say whose nest it was originally. This is how hedgehogs pick up fleas and other parasites left behind by previous visitors.

Summer nests may be quite flimsy structures but may sometimes involve the collection of grass, paper, leaves and other debris to construct something resembling the hibernation nest. Much depends on the weather and the site chosen to spend the day. It is very rare to find two hedgehogs occupying the same nest at once (though they often do so in captivity). During warm weather, a nest may not be built at all; the hedgehog just lies up hidden in a grass tussock or under a pile of leaves. Casual 'nesting' like this makes them very vulnerable to strimmers, the machines with a whirling cord used to destroy patches of weeds and long vegetation.

There is no doubt that hedgehogs know where they are going. They don't just wander at random. The repeated reappearance of marked animals in our gardens shows this. People have also 'deported' marked animals from their gardens and let them go, only to see them return the next night from distances of at least a quarter of a mile (400 metres). One radio-tracked hedgehog was removed from her nest and walked that distance more or less non-stop back to her family of young, and later retraced her steps to a favourite feeding area. How she accomplished this is a mystery. Scent trails would be difficult to follow, being criss-crossed by many other animals; there were no direct paths and no obvious visual cues. Clearly hedgehogs have a good sense of direction. We have seen the same thing with captive animals released in an unfamiliar place. They quickly find their way about and manage to locate the previous night's nest without apparent difficulty, even though the whole area is completely new to them.

By following the same hedgehogs for weeks or even months one can get an idea of how much general space they need. If all their movements are marked on a map, the total area of a male hedgehog's

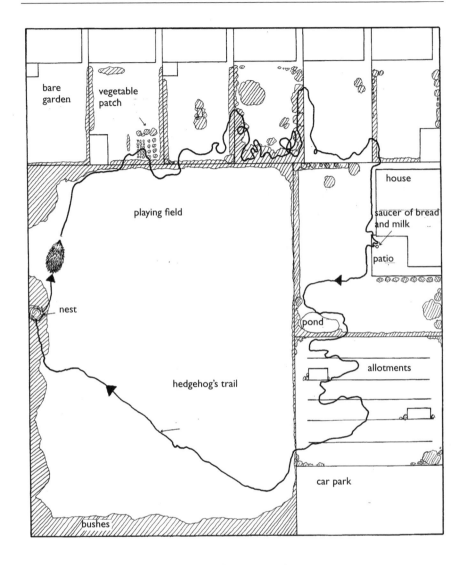

*Typical night's meanderings*

normal stomping ground seems to be about 20-30 hectares (60 acres or so). Females make do with much less (10 hectares/30 acres). Biologists call an animal's normally used area its 'home range', but this is a fairly woolly concept, especially for hedgehogs. Some hedgehogs stay in much the same place and use a similar area from month to month or even in successive years. Others appear to be 'of no fixed abode' and wander widely and unpredictably. Sometimes they abruptly vanish altogether. This is a particular irritation when the animal is carrying a radio transmitter that cost £150 and cannot now be located.

People often confuse the idea of 'home range' with that of 'territory'. While the former is a normal area of activity, territory is only that part of the area that an animal actually defends. Birds often have territories (one robin will chase another from its patch of garden lawn for example) and some mammals do too. Yet if you follow hedgehogs night after night, you find their paths cross and intermingle. None of the animals appears to defend its own patch and keep out other hedgehogs; they all wander freely at will. In this sense, hedgehogs do not have a territory; yet they often fight if they meet. It's quite likely that hedgehogs are non-territorial by the conventional definitions, but do defend the immediate space around where they happen to be. Hedgehogs need elbow room, not an empire. Subordinate hedgehogs can use the same areas as the dominant ones, just so long as they do so at a different time and keep out of the way. Feral (gone-wild) cats appear to have a similar social organization.

Some animals, otters for example, leave their droppings as territorial signposts: animal 'keep out' notices to warn off trespassers. Dogs leave their scent messages on lamp-posts. So far as we know, hedgehogs don't do these things. They leave their droppings apparently at random and it's impossible to say where they urinate because it's done so unobtrusively. Nevertheless, the hedgehog has a keen nose and is bound to be capable of recognizing the smell of other hedgehogs and their products. Perhaps this is all they do, merely noting who is about and who has passed by recently. This is all that is really necessary if they are not defending territorial areas. When you think about it, there is no real need for hedgehogs to be territorial, especially in suburban areas where there is plenty of food. Why bother to waste energy defending a territory if you don't need to?

## Why are hedgehogs nocturnal?
The hedgehog's spines are such good protection against predators that there seems little need to be active only under cover of darkness, hence the

question. We ask such a question because we presume that being active in daylight is the norm and animals doing anything else require some sort of explanation. In fact, from a biological point of view, it's the other way round. Nocturnal behaviour is the norm for mammals in general and has been ever since they first evolved. It's diurnal behaviour that's special and needs explanation. True, the hedgehog could get away with being active in daylight, and often does, but there is no positive advantage in doing so and a serious problem. Most of the small invertebrate animals that form the natural food of the hedgehog are, for their own reasons, nocturnal. Some need to avoid daytime warmth and sunshine to cut down on their water loss by evaporation, and many benefit from moist, dew-laden night air. Most of them come out in the dark to try to avoid being seen and eaten. So the reason why hedgehogs are nocturnal is simply that most of their food is too. There would be no advantage in changing a habit pursued over millions of years.

# Breeding and raising a family

The hedgehog's breeding season lasts from about April until September. The main period of activity is usually in May and June when the nights are warm. It is at this time that you are most likely to hear the loud, rhythmic snorting of 'courting' hedgehogs in the garden. So loud is the noise that people have often woken up and gone to their open bedroom windows to see what was going on out in the flower beds.

'Courtship' is a grandiose term for what is actually a rather ill-tempered and seemingly tedious affair. What happens is that a male, encountering a female, will begin to circle round her. She, with dogged perversity, will turn to keep her flank towards him. Undeterred, he continues to press his suit, while she constantly rebuffs him. The pair of them repeatedly shuffle round and round in circles. This palaver may go on for hours, though usually ends abruptly and prematurely with one or other animal running off. The whole rigmarole is accompanied by the characteristic, regular puffing and snorting noises emitted mainly by the female as she repulses the male, although he may snort too.

*Hedgehog courtship*

*Rival male coming to join in the fun*

Not surprisingly, all this noise tends to attract attention, and not just from householders woken from their sleep. Frequently other male hedgehogs turn up, perhaps intent on getting a slice of the action. Courtship is thus often interrupted by the arrival of a fresh suitor, whereupon there is a brief intermission while he is dealt with. The two males square up to each other and may indulge in head-butting, banging each other about; one may even be chased off. Sometimes the new male wins the sparring match, sometimes both lose because the female does a bunk while the two males are not looking.

There is an old joke which poses the question, 'How do hedgehogs mate?' The answer is, 'Carefully;' and this is not far from the truth. With such a spiny partner, mating is not something to be undertaken lightly or without considerable co-operation from the female. In fact she has to adopt a special posture, belly pressed flat to the ground, and back arched downwards so that her nose points skywards. Her spines must be laid flat. Neglect of any of these factors renders mating impossible and at any time the female can bristle her spines or throw the male off. For his part the male mounts the female from behind, gripping the spines over her shoulders with his teeth and scrabbling with his paws to get a better position. His own back must be arched into a most unhedgehog-like shape in order to get all the angles right for successful mating. And after all that, conception falls well short of a sure-fire certainty. Many females still fail to become pregnant, even after several matings, and a fair proportion may escape becoming pregnant altogether.

There is no evidence that any sort of pair bond is formed between male and female hedgehogs (although this has been suggested by some writers). The male stays with the female after mating for only a few hours, if that. Sometimes he (or she) may pair up with another partner the very same night. Complete promiscuity appears to be the rule. A study by Nigel Reeve showed that one male courted at least ten different females (some several times each) in two seasons and one female might have a dozen different mates.

Hedgehogs are not sexually mature in the year of their birth, so they do not indulge in this sort of thing until their second year. They are then capable of breeding every year until their deaths.

*Female has to be flat to help male to mate.*

Normally there are equal numbers of males and females in a population. However, if you take a sample of hedgehogs (e.g. by catching them in the garden or by collecting road casualties), the sex ratio is likely to be heavily biased towards males in the spring and early summer. This is not because there are more males, but simply due to the fact that they are more active at that time and therefore more likely to be found. Conversely, in the autumn females may predominate, apparently because males begin hibernating earlier, leaving more females to be caught. Baby hedgehogs occur in approximately equal numbers of both sexes at any time.

# Telling t'other from which

It is often assumed that the big, 'purposeful' hedgehogs are males; and they might be, but you can't be certain, any more than you can tell the sexes from the shape of the head. People who assert that it's a 'he' or a 'she' are fooling themselves unless they check. Sexing hedgehogs is easy, the difficult bit is getting them to uncurl; that's the problem. Gently lift a hunched hedgehog, sliding your two hands under it, one from each side. Then shuffle and toss it slightly into the air so that it uncurls a little to put its feet on to your hands to steady itself. Continue the gentle agitation, drawing your hands apart so that its front feet are on one hand and back feet on the other. After a while the hedgehog should be fully extended. Its front end can then be lifted, perhaps pressing its back against your own tummy at the same time. You can then carefully peep at its underside to compare with the diagrams here. At all times, move slowly and gently, keep your hands and fingers flat. If you are clumsy, the hedgehog will roll up, trapping your fingers inside, and that's painful! When you get the hang of it, 'hedgehog charming' is easy, although the occasional individual (and sometimes pregnant ones) may obstinately refuse to uncurl.

In adult male hedgehogs the penis appears as a large opening about where you would expect the navel to be: about 2" (5 cm) in front of the anus. In females the two openings are close together (only about 2cm apart, or less) and near to the base of the tail. Baby hedgehogs are more difficult to sex, especially when they are only a couple of months old, but at this age it hardly matters.

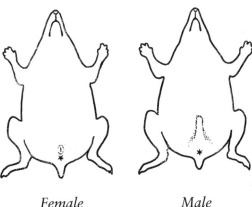

*Female*          *Male*

# Family life

When a female does become pregnant, she will have her babies after about four and a half weeks. Normally the gestation period of mammals is fairly fixed (nine months in humans for example), but in hedgehogs it is apparently rather variable. This may be due to the unpredictable British weather. A cold spell in the early spring may cause a shortage of food and a temporary resumption of hibernation. If the female went torpid, then the development of her embryos would be slowed down. When normal activity is resumed, embryo growth would pick up again but pregnancy would be lengthened by an amount corresponding to the period of torpor. This is only speculation; no research has been done on this intriguing possibility, but we do know that it happens in bats. These can be forced into 'summer hibernation' by cold weather and shortage of insect food, which imposes hibernation on bat embryos and lengthens the total time they take to develop. If something similar happened in hedgehogs it would be very unusual among mammals (and extremely interesting), but it would explain why hedgehog pregnancies seem to be of variable duration.

Most baby hedgehogs are probably born in June and July, perhaps a bit later in the north. Females that lose a litter for some reason, and also those that manage to raise a family early in the summer, are capable of conceiving a second litter. However, these are unlikely to be born before September and may come as late as October. They stand little chance of surviving the coming winter.

The average family size is about 4 or 5, although some females have 6 or even 7 babies. So, theoretically, one mother hedgehog could have 10 or more young in a year; but this would be unlikely. It is also unlikely that all of those young

*Spines in the newly born are hidden by pimples.*

# A hedgehog with fifteen babies!

In late July 1997, a lady told me she had been clearing shrubbery in the garden and disturbed a hedgehog in its nest. The following evening, a second (much bigger) hedgehog was seen in the same place, making a lot of noise. The next morning, the smaller female spent 2 hours making 14 journeys from the nest to another site, each time carrying a baby hedgehog, and a fifteenth baby was later found in the nest, dead.

It was assumed that the family had numbered 15 and the second hedgehog was the male coming to assist at a time of need. In fact, litters of more than 8 or 9 are exceedingly rare, and 15 has never been reported before. Moreover, males take no part in rearing their offspring. What seems more likely is that both these adults were females and somehow their litters had become combined. Aggregating young into crèches is known for some other species (including the dormouse), but I recall only one report for the hedgehog. This was in 1958 when a nest was found on the Isle of Wight containing 6 babies of two clearly different size categories. The explanation offered then was a form of superimposed pregnancy, but this is unlikely.

Perhaps the lady had actually disturbed two nests during the shrub clearance and the noise next day was the second female moving her young into a nest which was already occupied by the first hedgehog and her family (hedgehogs will use each other's nests, although usually only when they are empty). Maybe this caused the first hedgehog, dismayed by all this disturbance from people and another hedgehog, to move the entire collection of young. The problem then would be to rear any of them, as female hedgehogs often have difficulty raising even 6 young, never mind 14.

would survive. A more realistic expectation would be that the average mother manages to rear 2, perhaps 3 babies per season.

Giving birth to spiny babies could be a tricky business. Some books suggest that the problem is overcome by having very soft spines at birth, but

*First set of spines is white with a parting down the middle.*

even these would be a severe embarrassment if a baby was born tail first. It would just get stuck. This sometimes happens anyway, with fatal results. Actually the spines are covered by skin at birth and appear

*Dark spines grow up among the white.*

just as little pimples on the surface. Soon after birth, which only takes a minute or two, the baby's spines begin to appear, and the first set (about a hundred of them) are pure white. They grow in two distinct tracts with a parting down the middle of the back. Many books say these spines turn brown as the babies get older. This is wrong. The white spines stay white until they are moulted weeks or months later. What actually happens is that brown spines grow up among the white ones, wave after wave of them, until they swamp the first set. From about fifteen days old, the white ones are hardly visible.

The babies are born into a specially constructed nest, often under a shed or pile of garden debris. The nest is like a large version of the winter

*Ten-day old babies*

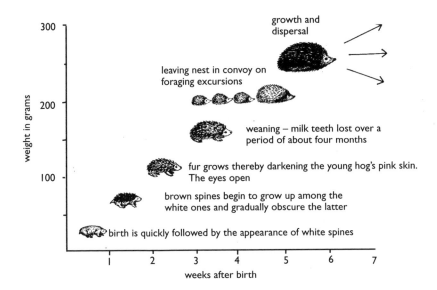

300

weight in grams

200

100

growth and dispersal

leaving nest in convoy on foraging excursions

weaning – milk teeth lost over a period of about four months

fur grows thereby darkening the young hog's pink skin. The eyes open

brown spines begin to grow up among the white ones and gradually obscure the latter

birth is quickly followed by the appearance of white spines

1    2    3    4    5    6    7

weeks after birth

nest, often made of leaves and grass and frequently incorporating bits of paper and other rubbish. No special material is collected to line it, although trampling around inside tends to soften and crumble the inner layers of the nest and ensure that the nest chamber is smooth inside. If the mother is disturbed within the first few hours after birth she is likely to desert or eat her babies. Later, when they are bigger, she may react to disturbance by carrying them off to another nest, holding each baby in her teeth by the scruff of its neck.

Baby hedgehogs are born blind and are pale pink. At two weeks old, their eyes open and by that time they not only have plenty of brown spines but their skin is also darker in colour. They have milk teeth, just like human babies, and these begin to be replaced in the third week of life. The last milk tooth is lost after about three or four months. The mother feeds her babies on milk of course, for which purpose she has five pairs of nipples; easily enough outlets for the largest family. Nevertheless it's quite likely that available milk is sufficient to support no more than four or five young. In very dry or cold weather, the mother herself may be short of food and even less able to support her entire family. About one in five of all baby hedgehogs die before they even leave the nest, members of larger litters being particularly at risk.

*A mother leads her young on a feeding foray.*

When they are three to four weeks old, young hedgehogs are big enough to leave the nest and go on foraging trips with the mother. A female leading a little procession of prickly babies is a charming sight and a welcome sign that they have survived one of the most difficult periods of their lives. The babies soon learn what to eat, but return to the nest to take their mother's milk as well. Gradually, over a period of about ten days, the family splits up as the young ones wander off on their own. At this stage they weigh about 8oz (250g), ten times their weight at birth. From conception to weaning is only about two months. In that time each baby has been fed mainly by milk from its mother. She has to provide enough nourishment for the 'manufacture' and maintenance of over 2lb (a kilo) of hedgehogs (more than her own weight) as well as herself. It must be a tremendous strain and it is hardly surprising that twenty per cent of the young don't make it.

Once the family has dispersed, brothers and sisters are unlikely to live together again, for hedgehogs live solitary lives. Nor are they likely to meet their father because he has played no part in raising his offspring and it's difficult to see how he could ever recognize them as his own – and vice versa. Hedgehogs meet and pass each other like ships in the night. There's no more to it than that.

# Autumn orphans

Some female hedgehogs give birth to late litters, in September or even October. By the time these babies are old enough to leave the nest, winter is nearly upon them. They are faced with the almost insuperable problem of finding enough to eat at the very time of year when nights are getting colder and natural food is becoming increasingly scarce. Wet and frosty nights just add to the misery.

The trouble is that the baby hedgehogs not only want enough food to live on from day to day, but need extra in order to double their size in the space of a few weeks. On top of that they need still more food to store as fat to keep them going during hibernation; all at a time when food supplies are diminishing. Clearly they can't make ends meet. Under these circumstances it is common to see baby hedgehogs

weighing only 5-7oz (150-200g) struggling against the odds to survive, often foraging in broad daylight. While the adults have long since gone into hibernation, these babies are forced to remain active well into the winter, even as late as Christmas. This is why the majority of hedgehogs seen after mid November seem to be small ones. The question is, what to do about them? The same goes for the nests of abandoned baby hedgehogs we sometimes find in the autumn during garden-tidying operations. Can we help the young to survive? Should we help? Perhaps it would be cruel to interfere and prevent them from hibernating?

The answer to these questions is simple: if we leave the babies alone they will almost certainly die. Hedgehogs need a certain minimum amount of stored fat to see them safely through the winter. My calculations show that they need to weigh about 1lb (450g). It would be better if they weighed more than this, but 1lb is the minimum weight necessary for survival. If they hibernate before reaching that weight they stand practically no chance of surviving. It follows then that to leave underweight baby hedgehogs to their own devices any time after late September effectively condemns them to death. Taking them into captivity and giving them artificial food may be unnatural, but at least they may live (see the next section for details of rearing baby hedgehogs). Some people claim that hedgehogs need to weigh 1lb 4oz(600g) in order to survive the winter. Obviously the bigger they are the better their chances. However, many can and do survive after hibernating at lower weights than this. To set 1lb 4oz(600g) as a vital threshold encourages people to take into care many hedgehogs that do not need to be 'rescued'. Moreover, 600g is a high target to set for young of the year to reach. Relatively few juveniles can reach that weight in the time available after they leave the nest. Once the babies have attained the necessary weight they can be released. Preferably this should be done during a mild period so the shock is not too great. The important thing is to ensure that they have access to dry nesting material and a suitable place to build a winter home. Ideally this should be a woodland or shrubby area with plenty of leaves (see p. 140) but in your garden, a sheet of hardboard propped against the fence or behind the shed would make a suitable shelter. Old newspaper forms an excellent substitute for leaves as nest material. Probably the hedgehog won't stay where you put it because it finds a better place, and that's all to the good.

Juveniles, overwintered in captivity, will have had little or no experience of feeding and nesting in the wild. They might suffer and die after release. It is a relief to report that our studies reveal that these inexperienced animals can, and do, cope amazingly well after release and soon become absorbed into the wild hedgehog community.

# Keeping hedgehogs and rearing babies

On the whole, hedgehogs don't make particularly good pets (being messy and rather unresponsive creatures), but may be fun to keep for a while. Baby hedgehogs are often taken in by well meaning people and they may well owe their lives to their kindly foster parents. This particularly applies to underweight juveniles rescued from the oncoming winter. Sometimes it is necessary to keep a hedgehog for a while, pending its transfer to a proper animal hospital. So, some hints on hedgehog-keeping will not come amiss. However, these notes are intended only as suggestions for temporary accommodation. Hedgehogs belong in the wild and should not be kept as pets for any length of time. Looking after them, especially babies, is a difficult job, best left to experts with plenty of experience. You can get advice or find your nearest hedgehog carer by consulting the British Hedgehog Preservation Society or the RSPCA (see p. 203).

Hedgehogs will live in quite a small cage, but obviously they prefer more space if possible. They can always be allowed out for exercise around the house, although they are often not well house trained. It is important that their cage or pen does not have bars or wire mesh on the floor; a hedgehog's feet are soft and will suffer damage unless a softer floor is provided. Newspaper, sawdust, earth, peat, even old carpet: all are suitable but need to be changed fairly frequently. Remember that hedgehogs can dig, so a simple pen in the garden won't hold them if they can tunnel under the walls. Remember too that they can climb. Wire mesh is easy, even boards or bricks are not escape-proof, although a strip of metal or plastic rainwater gutter fixed along the top of the walls offers a bulging smooth curve to climb over and can't easily be negotiated (but watch out at the corners). Although they are nocturnal in the wild, hedgehogs can be persuaded in captivity to emerge in daylight, by feeding them only during the daytime.

# Pet 'pigmy hedgehogs'

These are African white fronted hedgehogs (*Atelerix albiventris*). They are widely kept as 'novelty pets' in the USA and several dedicated pet-keeper's manuals have been published. An American pet supplier claimed that the African Pygmy Hedgehog was 'the HOT! New exotic pet of the 90s' and offered '13 good reasons' for owning one. These included the information that they need little space ('a 20 gallon aquarium or equivalent') and that they are quiet and non-destructive ('as a hedgehog doesn't hurt walls, curtains or carpets').

Coming originally from dry semi-desert habitats, they seem better adapted to life in captivity than our European species. In particular they will eat dry pelleted foods (which are less messy than the European hedgehog's diet), they are also smaller and seem to survive quite well in small cages with sawdust for bedding. They are widely sold in American pets shops and may occasionally be seen for sale in Europe. I saw some in a Paris street market once, ranging from pale grey to pure white, as though someone had been selectively breeding them to create new colour varieties. The fact remains, European hedgehogs don't make suitable pets.

In the wild, hedgehogs drink often, so water should be available. If you give them an open bowl, they will stomp in it and make a mess. Use a water bottle from a pet shop, one that delivers water as drips. A wooden or cardboard box should be provided, lying on its side, and plenty of newspaper which the hedgehog will shred and carry to its box to make a nest. The nest box should have a roof or the nesting material becomes scattered. Regular handling will persuade some animals to become very tame (see p. 83 for sexing and handling hedgehogs); but others remain totally intractable. It does no harm to remove ticks and fleas (see p. 47, 50). Adult hedgehogs are no problem to look after and feed; the real difficulties come with trying to raise babies. Sometimes a nest is accidentally disturbed in the garden revealing a mother and her family. They are best left alone and she will carry them to a fresh home. If no mother is present, or if babies are brought in by the dog, you may decide to try and rear them. If they are so young that they are still blind, there is little hope for them, though they may survive if you are lucky. If they are old enough to have brown spines, there is a better chance of success. But don't be surprised if they die, hedgehogs are very vulnerable creatures until they are at least 6-8 weeks old and at least a fifth of them die before that age even under natural circumstances.

People have successfully raised hedgehogs on tinned milk and various baby foods, but the mother's milk is more than just food. For the first few days after birth, baby hedgehogs receive a lot of immune proteins in their milk supply and these help protect from infections and gut disorders. Cow's milk and other substitutes lack these ready-made natural medicines and so the young hedgehog is very susceptible to infections that may easily prove fatal. Cow's milk should not be given to captive baby hedgehogs anyway as it causes diarrhoea and they may die. Suitable food can be prepared from human baby foods, made into a runny liquid with a food blender and diluted with water or Lectade. The liquid should be offered from a pipette, a dropper or a plastic syringe. The young hoglets will soon learn to drink from it, but will need feeding every few hours or so. They should be persuaded to lap from a dish as soon as possible, then they will be less trouble to look after.

When they are about three weeks old, with eyes open and a body

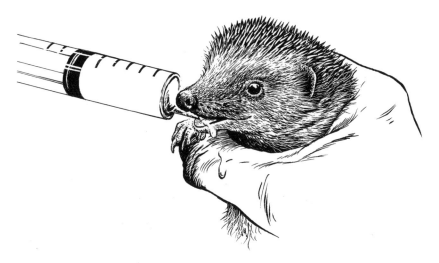

*Feeding a baby using a plastic syringe*

weight of 4oz (100g) or more, baby hedgehogs should be persuaded to diversify their diet. Scrambled egg is a welcome treat; also bread soaked in gravy, the juice out of fresh liver; anything semi-liquid and rich in protein and as varied as possible. My hedgehogs rather liked crumbled chocolate biscuits. Later they can graduate on to tinned dog food, two or three big tablespoonsful twice a day should be enough. You can also buy tins and packets of special hedgehog food (called 'Spike's Dinner') from pet shops, but it works out a bit expensive if your animal is hungry! An adult needs about 8oz (200g) of food per day if it is to grow and fatten up. The natural diet is very varied, so it is a good idea to 'dilute' or extend tinned foods by mashing in puppy meal, table scraps or broken biscuits. Soft fruit, bread or small amounts of cake go down well too. Add a little water to stop the mixture being too dry. A few people have reported trouble following the use of fish-based cat foods, so perhaps it's best to avoid these if possible. Never feed peanuts to hedgehogs (unless they are crushed into small pieces) as they can get stuck in the animal's jaws and prevent them feeding.

Healthy hedgehogs will thrive on a mixed diet like this and gain weight rapidly. One of mine, rescued as a baby from near death, was soon putting on weight at an average of $\frac{1}{3}$oz (10g) per day and ultimately grew to be the biggest one-year-old hedgehog I've ever seen; then he escaped!

Little hedgehog treats are always welcome, and here individual preferences become evident. Some love meal-worms (unfortunately, because they are expensive), others like bits of chicken. I heard of one that was partial to mandarin oranges and knew another that would do anything for crushed salted peanuts. Perhaps oddest of all was Emily. She loved cow's milk, so much so that when the BBC tried to film her eating worms, she would only oblige if they were first dipped in milk. She then attacked them eagerly, but only to lick the milk off; she left the worms.

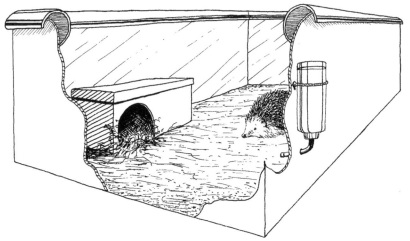

*Pen for keeping hedgehogs*

You can perform some interesting experiments to determine hedgehog likes and dislikes. Unfortunately some individuals become very fussy and refuse to eat dog food and other sensible food and insist on a special diet. They should be discouraged from becoming too fixed on one particular thing, partly because it's a nuisance and partly because they are then likely to be less adaptable and able to look after themselves if they escape or are released.

However, food is only part of the problem with young hedgehogs.

For them, the secret of success is to keep them warm. This is vital. Babies have a large surface area through which they lose body heat, and next to no insulation to prevent this happening. If they cool down, then their bodily functions begin to get slower so digestion for example takes longer to release food energy. Their movements get slower, which means that the muscles produce less heat and the body cools still more. Quite soon the baby hedgehog is trapped in a downward spiral of getting colder and slower and it dies over a period of a few days, like a run-down clockwork toy. Obviously this is a major threat to babies on cold nights in late summer and early autumn, a time when shortage of food may leave them in trouble anyway. Even quite big hedgehogs may suffer this cooling-down syndrome if they are sickly.

Warmth will stimulate them, raise their level of activity and may help them 'turn the corner' on to the road to viability. But do not provide warmth in the form of a desk lamp or something similar shining down. The best way is to wrap a hot water bottle in a couple of layers of blanket and let the hedgehogs nestle down on top or against it. This bathes them in all-round warmth without glaring light. Try to keep the temperature similar to that inside your own pockets by renewing the hot water every few hours. It's probably best not to use electrically heated pads (like electric blankets) as these are not designed to resist hedgehogs weeing on them. Anyway, electricity and hedgehog drinking bowls make a dangerous mixture. However, if the heated pad can be kept outside the cage (for example underneath), then this could be an ideal way of maintaining a gentle background warmth. Give the animals clean blankets every couple of days.

Within a few weeks of being well fed, young hedgehogs may grow fat enough to survive hibernation out of doors (free or in captivity), but it will do them no harm if they are kept indoors without hibernating. It may be 'unnatural' not to hibernate but not harmful. Indeed since a good third of all hedgehogs probably die in hibernation, captive ones may well be better off without it. It is a mistake to assume that hedgehogs need to be kept warm in hibernation. In fact, warmth might be the very last thing they want. Laboratory studies show that the best temperature for hibernation is 4°C. Colder than that risks frostbite, and warmer means the hedgehogs use up their fat reserves faster.

This is because the speed of a chemical reaction (including metabolism and the use of fat within the body) doubles for every 10° rise in temperature. So a hedgehog kept in the spare room or a warm conservatory may use up its fat twice as fast as one that is hibernating in colder conditions. The fat reserves will run out sooner and the animal will be at risk of starvation, long before it actually wakes up in the spring. So it is not a kindness to put hibernating animals anywhere except in a cold place.

When you decide to release your hedgehog, it is best to choose a place where hedgehogs are likely to be reasonably common already such as parks, old cemeteries, farmland, big gardens – places with plenty of worms, bushes and trees. Try to put out some food for a few nights after release to help introduction to new surroundings; it can't do any harm, although they may well ignore it. Choose a period of warm, muggy weather if possible. This will help ensure that there is plenty of natural food about and your animal is not inconvenienced by being cold itself. Remember that hedgehogs need dry leaves and a sheltered place (e.g. bottom of hedge, under a shed, deep in a thicket) to build a good winter nest, so try to choose a place with these features too. Avoid the vicinity of busy roads if you can, but remember that hedgehogs wander far and wide so there's not much point in choosing one place rather than another just because it's 100 yards further away from traffic. They are not bothered about noise; two hedgehogs I studied chose daytime nests only a few paces from a very busy dual carriageway with fast cars and lorries going by at a rate of one every few seconds.

# Getting hedgehogs tame

Some hedgehogs are unco-operative and that's that. However, others will become very tame indeed, especially those that have been reared by hand from an early age. They will then not roll up or 'bristle' and will allow at least their owners to tickle their tummies and turn them upside down, feet in the air, things that normally meet with severe hedgehog disapproval. I know one animal (Georgie, star of a BBC-TV film) who would come out of her nest box when called by name; but another (Emily, who had also been hand reared) who often bit me.

There is so much individuality among hedgehogs that one cannot generalize and say 'this is right' or 'this is wrong'. However, as a rule, sudden noises and clumsy handling are the two things most likely to upset hedgehogs. They normally don't like bright lights either. Regular handling is helpful: firm, but gentle. Avoid sudden movements and touching their faces. Handling when they are fed is a good idea; they then associate you with food. The next step is to reward good behaviour with some favourite morsel, the problem being that hedgehogs' tastes differ. Georgie loved salted peanuts, Emily liked milk, others are eager for mealworms while some won't bother with them.

# Rehabilitating hedgehogs – does it work?

Over the last 20 years there has been a huge increase in the number of people caring for orphaned, sick or injured hedgehogs. Partly this is due to an increased awareness of the threats that face wildlife and a real desire to help. Hedgehogs are peculiarly vulnerable to many modern hazards that seldom threaten other mammals. For example, strimmers and mowing machines that are used to cut the rough vegetation where hedgehogs lie up during summer days cause serious injuries to hedgehogs. Limbs may be amputated, the head scalped or a large patch of skin sliced away from the animal's back as it lies curled up in its nest. Unlike many other injured animals, hedgehogs are easy to find and pick up without risk of being bitten. Young born too late in the year to fatten up sufficiently to survive hibernation (see p. 89) are also taken into captivity to be cared for over winter. It is also a fact that much more information is now available and many more vets seem willing to become involved too. We even have specialised wildlife hospitals, as well as the RSPCA, animal clinics and hedgehog rescue centres (the British Hedgehog Preservation Society can provide details of your local hedgehog carers, see p. 203).

Hedgehogs are very tough animals and seem to survive injuries that would kill other things much sooner. Nevertheless, several thousand sick, injured or baby hedgehogs are now taken into care every year by well meaning people and it is common to find people looking after ten or more at once. One kindly lady was recently reported to have cared for 18,000 hedgehogs in the previous 14 years. In Jersey, Dru Burdon cared for over 3,000 hedgehogs in 9 years and released more than two thirds of them, equivalent to 3% of the entire population of the island. The hedgehog is also one of the most frequent patients in Britain's wildlife hospitals. As a result of all this, a lot of time, money and effort is expended on nursing them back to health, often with much emotional commitment too. But what then? Is it all a sentimental waste of time or do 'rehabilitated' hedgehogs manage to survive after release back into the wild?

Another question is, what should we do about severely disabled animals? Garden strimmers for example can slice off the snout of a hedgehog or amputate a limb. The animal may still live and the wound will heal, but the creature is left with an important part of its anatomy missing. Perhaps euthanasia is the best option for such animals? But some carers say that they are in the business of saving animals, not killing them and that to save the most severe cases helps emphasise the value of life. Maybe, but even with humans there is an increasing feeling that quality of life must also be taken into account. For many species, the question does not arise. Release of a three-legged rabbit or squirrel for example, would be to condemn it to an early death at the teeth of some predator. However, this is less true for the hedgehog whose spines protect it well. I have found three legged hedgehogs still alive and apparently surviving, though loss of the snout would be a more serious problem for an animal so dependent upon its sense of smell. It is not at all clear what is the right thing to do, nor can we easily construct rules that apply equally to all species. However, some carers use walled gardens as release sites for severely disabled hedgehogs, allowing them to roam more widely than if they had been kept in a cage indefinitely.

The aim of most animal carers is to return their charges to the wild at the earliest suitable opportunity. However, by then a hedgehog will have become accustomed to artificial food. Perhaps it will no longer be able to find sufficient natural prey to survive, especially

# A royal hedgehog carer

Apparently, Lady Sarah Lennox nearly became Queen of England in 1756 because the young King George III took a fancy to her. However, he was very firmly advised to marry a foreigner, for political benefits to be gained, and Sarah got dumped. She was very hurt and transferred her affections to a squirrel and a sick hedgehog, which she insisted on bringing down to breakfast each day.

if it has been released in an unfamiliar place or habitat. Hedgehogs released far from their original home may simply try to return and wander about hungry and disoriented. (They are certainly very good at 'homing', at least over distances of up to half a mile/1km). Will they be able to build a nest successfully and, if so, will they be able to find it again? Will they be rejected by the resident wild hedgehogs into whose area they are released? These are real problems that could simply condemn them to a lingering death. Maybe 'rehabilitation' is not a kindness after all, but a waste of time and hedgehogs, even perhaps a bit cruel?

Over the years I have carried out a series of experiments to find out whether rehabilitated hedgehogs can cope after release back into the wild. In the first study, three adults were taken 180 miles(300km) north to Yorkshire and released there in woodland. They were radio tracked to find out where they went and they were checked each night to see whether they managed to feed well enough to maintain their weight. Fortunately they didn't attempt to head back home and it was marvellous to see how quickly they learned to find their way about. They built nests and returned to them unerringly. They travelled a kilometre or more each night, just as wild hedgehogs do (despite having been confined to small cages for many weeks beforehand). They also behaved normally with the local wild hedgehogs, often indulging in long courtship sessions, and there was no sign of their being attacked or driven away. However, after three weeks, only one had managed to keep up its body weight and the others were still getting thinner. We had to leave them without knowing whether they survived or not.

A longer study was obviously needed, using more animals. This

time eight hedgehogs were taken from RSPCA centres in London and released in farmland around Flatford Mill in Suffolk. Again (happily!) the animals did not head off back to London, and again they managed to nest and find their way about. One ran away to the village gardens over half a mile distant and had put on weight when last seen three weeks after release. Indeed most of the animals were doing well, but two months after release, only one of them was still living near the Mill, and she had put on weight. Others were still alive and apparently doing well, having lost weight at first, but then showed more constant weights than the local wild hedgehogs! At least two of the released hedgehogs swam the river Stour and another fell into the millpond lock. I had to climb down the lock gates in the dark to retrieve it, at some risk of ending up in the drink myself. One of the females was later found greedily exploiting the waste bins behind a small café, some 2½ miles(4km) from the release point, having increased its weight by over 10%. Ironically we later found her dead in the road by the village signboard saying 'Dedham'! But that could have happened to any hedgehog, and this one had been doing well up until then.

Most of the released animals had scattered widely, and some of them were reported by the public from over 2 miles away. Clearly they were fit enough to travel so far, but maybe these London hedgehogs were seeking more familiar surroundings than the fields around Flatford. Perhaps hedgehogs ought to be released in the same sort of habitat from which they originally came.

Our results are very encouraging, but we know little about the fate of hedgehogs released in town gardens and parks because few people attempt to find out what happens to them. If they wander about, the hedgehogs will inevitably leave the park or garden release site and cross roads. They will then be at risk of being killed by traffic. I was told of a group of six released 'safely' on a secure school playing field, surrounded by houses and gardens, but one was killed by a car within three weeks. It is important to learn more about releases in towns, if only to advise people not to release hedgehogs into unfamiliar places in urban areas, no matter how safe they might seem to be. A possible exception is letting hedgehogs go in a walled garden. The problem here is that wild hedgehogs normally travel over ½ mile/1km in a night and have a home range of at least 5ha for females and three times that for males. A walled garden is too small and likely also to lead to squabbling if more than one hedgehog is present.

# Can inexperienced animals cope with release into the wild?

All this applies to rehabilitated adult hedgehogs that have some experience of life in the wild and know what to do. What about rescued juveniles (for example underweight animals that were too small to survive the winter out of doors) and babies raised in captivity who have never been free? These animals may never have been out of doors, never built their own nest, never seen a worm or other natural food, never travelled more than the few centimetres across their cage. They may also never have been alone before. Can they cope after being released? To find out, we radio tracked 12 overwintered juveniles from the RSPCA, due for release anyway on a farm in Devon on April 1st (an auspicious date!). Several had weighed less than 5 oz(150g) when first acquired the previous autumn and may never have been out of their mother's nest. Others had been brought to the RSPCA accompanied by their mother, whose nest had been destroyed. These hedgehogs would have had little or no experience of foraging or eating natural food, and certainly no experience of constructing their own nests.

The hedgehogs were all given a full health check, fitted with radio transmitters and released in a cow pasture on steep, rolling farmland with hedges and earth banks. There were wild hedgehogs also living here and signs of badgers, but there was no sett on the farm itself. Badgers live in high numbers throughout south-west England, so avoiding them was not a realistic option. The hedgehogs were found and weighed each night for five weeks. The weather was wet on most nights, probably the first rain these hedgehogs had ever encountered, and temperatures fell to -2°C, so conditions were quite challenging for hedgehogs and humans alike.

Several of the animals travelled more than ¼mile(½kilometre) per night and three made abrupt long-distance dispersal journeys of more than ½ mile(1 km), after being resident on the release area for several nights. Most of the hedgehogs lost weight following their release, in one case nearly 38%. This caused us considerable concern. Their steady decline in weight suggested that these animals were starving, but none returned regularly to feed at the pre-release cages. Some engaged in lengthy interactions with other hedgehogs instead of feeding and most of the animals also retired to their nests well before dawn, after a short night. All this suggests that starvation was not sufficiently serious to make feeding a priority activity. None of the animals remained active in daylight, a frequent sign of starvation in wild hedgehogs. Actually, they were not starving at all, just losing weight. In fact they had all become rather fat in captivity and weighed substantially more than wild juveniles at this time of year. The weight loss was nothing more serious than shedding excess fat. Weights stabilised at a more normal level after about 3-4 weeks and fluctuated less than in the local wild hedgehogs.

The ability to construct a nest and to find it again after a night's activity are two important criteria by which the success of rehabilitation may be assessed. Daytime nest positions were therefore located whenever possible. It was amazing to find these inexperienced animals were able to build normal nests and find them again, having never done this before nor been anywhere near this place. The pattern of nest use was normal, with male hedgehogs changing nests more frequently than females, and the animals often found their way back to old nests after an absence of several nights. At least two released animals found and used sites known to have been previously occupied by wild hedgehogs. Courtship behaviour was observed between our animals and wild hedgehogs, and also between each other, another new experience for them. Two might even have become pregnant.

## A spooky coincidence

One of the Devon hogs was particularly energetic, travelling all over the place. She was christened 'Freya' after the famous woman explorer Freya Stark. The hedgehog was killed on the same day that her namesake died after a long and eventful life.

Self-anointing was also observed among the released animals. There were no serious aggressive encounters among any of the hedgehogs, despite the relatively high population density that resulted from 12 additional animals being released close to each other, as well as the wild hedgehogs already present.

Overall, it was clear that the released hedgehogs were coping amazingly well, despite their lack of previous experience. The bad news is that two of our hedgehogs were run over (despite the local lanes having little traffic after dark!) and three more were killed and eaten by badgers. This was unfortunate, but it could have happened to any hedgehogs irrespective of their origin. The risk might have been increased because our animals were accustomed to being caught and handled. They might have been insufficiently wary of 'attack' and several barely bothered to roll up when they were caught for weighing each night. This would be dangerously casual behaviour when accosted by a badger. On the other hand, three of the local wild hedgehogs were also found dead and eaten by badgers. The killing was probably the work of only one badger passing by, as all the predation took place within a few nights. Moreover, the farm had been used previously for releasing hedgehogs and there were still some living there, despite the badgers.

When the results of this study were published, I was attacked in the newspapers (by hedgehog carers among others), for being irresponsible! It was said that hedgehogs should not have been released where badgers were present, nor near to roads. Yet badgers

are increasingly common and there are few places suitable for hedgehogs that lack them. Similarly it is almost impossible to find anywhere more than ½ mile /1km from a road, and hedgehogs often travel more than that in a night. Such criticism is unrealistic. If there is irresponsibility it lies with those who make no attempt at all to find out what happens to released animals. We have at least followed up the hedgehogs and it should be no surprise to learn that the world is full of dangers. Roads, predators and many other factors threaten survival. Natural mortality among hedgehogs is 20-30% per year. We can rehabilitate hedgehogs, but we cannot confer immortality and many will die. To believe otherwise is wishful thinking.

Many people would like to believe that released animals live long and happy lives. Such a belief persists precisely because proper follow-up studies are rare. The lack of information about rehabilitated animals may also be because many carers would probably rather not know what happens to their animals after release. The RSPCA is to be commended for having grasped this nettle, and not criticised for helping us to confirm that animals face many dangers in the wild.

The key point is that at least a third of our animals survived a minimum of two and a half months after release, despite having had no previous experience in the wild. If the RSPCA had not taken them into care the previous autumn, none of them would have survived at all.

## More releases, on Jersey

Later I repeated this study with inexperienced juvenile hedgehogs on Jersey (where badgers are absent), and more than 75% survived for the whole of the six-week study. One animal very sensibly moved swiftly to live near a local pub, another was found on the coast several weeks later over 3 miles(5km) away, feeding at food bowls put out for stray cats. The local hedgehog lady, Dru Burdon, has been caring for hundreds of sick and injured local hedgehogs and marking them when they were returned to the wild. Some of her animals have lived at least a year following release, and one survived more than five years. Most, perhaps all, would have died but for her help.

## Some observations and advice on releasing hedgehogs

1. Even inexperienced overwintered juvenile hedgehogs can and do survive release into the wild surprisingly well. Their rehabilitation is therefore a justifiable use of resources.

2. They can find natural foods with which they are unfamiliar, build nests and find them again; they also integrate well with each other and with wild hedgehogs living on site.

3. Nevertheless, released animals are vulnerable to the same dangers that threaten wild hedgehogs, perhaps more so because of their relative tameness.

4. Substantial and sustained weight loss is to be expected, especially if they are overweight as a result of being well fed in captivity.

5. Release should not take place early in the year before evidence has been found of locally active wild hedgehogs and the worms, slugs and beetles are active at night.

6. If captive animals are active before late March, they should be weighed. If their weights exceed 1lb 8oz(700g), they should be fed minimally to encourage them to go back into hibernation. Otherwise they may become sexually active too early in the year and may be fretful in captivity.

7. The substantial weight losses observed in field studies, suggest that it may be unwise to release animals weighing less than about 1lb(500g). Feed them up a bit first to provide some fat reserves to tide them over during their period of adjustment to a new life.

8. Badgers are probably the only predators sufficiently strong to kill significant numbers of hedgehogs, so releases should if possible avoid places where they are common. This is becoming increasingly difficult as badgers are now widespread and numerous, especially in the south-west.

9. It is desirable to avoid release sites near to busy roads, but this too is difficult. Hedgehogs often travel over a mile in a night, easily within range of a road in most parts of the country. Nevertheless, many can and do survive living close to busy roads.

10. Hedgehogs destined for release should not be encouraged to become too tame.

# Use of markers on released hedgehogs

A study by biologists at Oxford University found that wild hedgehogs moved from their home area often dispersed after release, travelling up to 2 miles(3.6km), crossing main roads and even swimming across the River Thames.

My radio-tracking studies show that released hedgehogs cope surprisingly well, and at least a third can expect to survive more than two months after release. Two months is long enough to reveal whether the animals starve to death, but radio tracking for longer is difficult, making it hard to tell how long the animals might survive after that. Some released hedgehogs disperse over long distances and it is difficult to find where they have gone.

To address these problems, I had some weatherproof PVC tags made, each bearing an identification number and a request to notify a telephone number. Tags were glued to hedgehogs using 'Araldite' just before they were let go. During the summer and autumn of 1998, telephone calls reported 11 tagged hedgehogs seen by members of the public. These people were put in touch with those who released the hedgehogs, who were very pleased to hear that their animals had succeeded in adjusting to life after release.

The hedgehogs reported were mostly alive and well, but two were found dead. One was beside a busy main road, the other was killed by a badger. Five (out of 11) animals had dispersed more than 1.8 miles(3km), including one that was reported from 10 miles(15km) away, although it may have been misidentified. Dispersals involved crossing major roads and at least one river.

In Jersey, 1,000 rehabilitated hedgehogs were fitted with numbered ear tags before being released. Most were not seen again, but 150 of them were recovered later. Of these 47(31%) had survived more than one year after release, 11(7%) lived more than 3 years and one 5 years. These survival rates are similar to those found in normal wild hedgehog populations, so rehabilitation was completely successful. Animals that would mostly have died from sickness or injury had been given a second chance at living and succeeded.

# Hedgehogs in the garden

There is no doubt at all that the hedgehog is the gardener's ally. It eats countless insect pests and does no harm. There is thus every reason to give hedgehogs all the encouragement we can to get them to live in and around our gardens. Besides, they make amusing and interesting visitors to our patios on summer evenings. Unfortunately many of us, well meaning towards hedgehogs in every other respect, don't make life easy for them at all. Indeed, without realizing it, we may easily turn our gardens into hedgehog death traps. It's silly to put out food for them only to find that they are claimed as victims of the

*Hedgehogs make themselves at home in our gardens and often benefit from food bowls put out for pets.*

garden pond. A survey in London suggested that nearly ten per cent of all dead hedgehogs reported had drowned: not because they can't swim but because they can't escape from some ponds. Smooth plastic pond liners and sheer-sided swimming pools are fatal. The best way to help hedgehogs if they fall into these things is to have a piece of wood floating as a life raft or (much better) one or two small strips of chicken wire dangling over the edge into the water. Hedgehogs can climb these like scrambling nets and make good their escape. A small pile of bricks in the corner of a pond will also allow escape.

A little bit of forethought will remove another potential hedgehog hazard: tennis nets. These are often left lying on the ground as a long sausage of net, or loose netting lying on the grass. Foraging hedgehogs easily get tangled up in this stuff and will die unless noticed and rescued. Try to keep tennis nets tied up off the ground when not in use. A similar problem exists with pea and strawberry nets, although here of course we can't lift the net out of reach or the birds will get in underneath. The solution is to peg the edges of the net down tightly. If the net is held taut, it is much less likely to become tangled round a hedgehog's feet and spines.

Tidy-mindedness is another problem. Gardeners like to sweep up dead leaves, root out brambles and keep their patches neat, but in doing so remove vital sites for winter nests and necessary nesting materials. Obviously few of us want a wilderness in our back yard just for the hedgehogs, but if we all keep our gardens surgically clean then the habitat becomes unsuitable for hedgehogs to live in permanently. This may be why people have hedgehogs for a few summer months and then lose them with the onset of winter; there is nowhere to make a suitable winter nest. The solution to this problem is constructive untidiness. Leave the fallen leaves behind the shed; don't dismantle the log pile down to ground level till early spring, by which time hibernators will be ready to wake up. Try to leave hedge bottoms alone and don't rake them out too often; leave odd corners and nooks; imagine yourself to be a hedgehog. Try also to be sparing, selective and sensible in the use of garden chemicals; remember what they do and remember that a hedgehog may see things differently to you.

Do be careful about using a strimmer. These nasty machines have

*Potential winter nest sites can be made by leaning a board against a wall or fence.*

become widespread since about 1980. They have a motor to drive a whirling cord which thrashes and chops down patches of long grass and weeds. They seem to be the ideal way of dealing with rank vegetation without resorting to chemical weedkillers. Unfortunately, our radio tracking shows that these patches of rough vegetation are exactly where hedgehogs choose to lie up during summer days. The strimmers inflict dreadful wounds on the animals, slicing off legs and noses among sleeping hedgehogs. I saw one animal that had been so scalped by a strimmer that its insides were visible through a large hole in its back. If you must use a strimmer, feel about in the weeds with your feet to make sure there are no hedgehogs already there.

# Nest boxes

Various suppliers of wildlife accessories offer to sell different types of nest boxes for hedgehogs. They can't do any harm and they do draw attention to the fact that hedgehogs need somewhere safe to nest, especially in winter. However, some designs are rather expensive and perhaps needlessly elaborate. They range from a simple tunnel made of plastic sheet that can be thrust under existing vegetation, to boxes and tubs made from quality materials. Some garden wildlife books even suggest designs that have a ventilation chimney and built-in flea trap. Some garden centres sell nest boxes that cost about £40, have smart hinges and look very nice; all they lack is a note put out for the milkman! Actually what the hedgehogs need is leaves or newspaper underneath some supporting structure like a pile of brushwood or a garden shed. Anything more elaborate is no more likely to be used. A paving stone raised on bricks at each corner will provide enough shelter and support, and you can stand a potted plant on top as well. Nests should be inspected with caution (or left alone) during the summer months as females with very young babies are liable to eat them or desert their family if they are disturbed. Hedgehogs hibernating there during the winter seem like they are dead, but if you tickle the spines gently, they will stiffen as the animal bristles. If the spines stay slack, smell your fingertips. Dead hedgehogs pong!

# Putting out food for garden hedgehogs

There must be thousands of people throughout the length and breadth of Britain who put out food each night for their hedgehogs, treating them as Honorary Members of the household, free-ranging pets. I wonder how many cows work full time to produce milk for the benefit of British hedgehogs? There are plenty of soft-hearted Continental householders too, and in Germany you can buy special packets of 'Igelfutter' (hedgehog food) in the shops, the British equivalent being tins of 'Spike's Dinner' or packets of freeze-dried insects, shrimps and fruits. These can be expensive. Dog food is cheaper and probably just as good.

Wild hedgehogs will readily visit a food bowl put out each evening. Initially they will come for it late, after house lights are out. But gradually they will get bolder and will soon learn to feed close to the house with light streaming on to them from the windows. The key thing is to ensure if possible that the food bowl is either always in the dark or always well lit. Try not to have some nights with curtains open and others with them closed. This will cause hesitancy among your hedgehog visitors until they get used to your habits. But remember, the 'hogs that come to your patio may not always be the same ones, so don't be surprised if 'it' seems to be tame one night and very shy another. Putting out grub for the hedgehogs gives a lot of pleasure to a lot of people and must contribute a fair bit to the total amount of food that passes down hedgehog throats. But is it a Good Thing? What effect does all this largesse have on the hedgehog population, bearing in mind that studies on other animals show that major biological factors such as breeding success and territory size are significantly affected by food availability.

Also there is the question of food suitability. Many people put out bread and milk for their hedgehogs, but could this actually be more harmful than helpful? And, how do you keep rats, cats and magpies

*Some hedgehogs will travel a long way for a bowl of food and probably enjoy considerable benefit from doing so.*

from eating it? These three major issues are explored further in the next few pages.

The same hedgehogs will come night after night, year after year, to eat food put out for them. They obviously welcome it, and it is reasonable to suppose that they do not travel further than necessary to get it. Thus, if food is regularly provided in a garden, you might assume the hedgehogs take up residence nearby, and that when they leave their nests each night, they make a 'bee line' straight for the food bowl so as to arrive as soon as possible, before other hedgehogs have eaten all the food. Most people I know who put out food for hedgehogs take these things for granted and further assume that 'their' hedgehogs, numbering only 2 or 3 at most, treat the garden and its precious food bowl as valuable territory and do not share these resources more than necessary with other hedgehogs. These assumptions are so logical that they must surely be true. In which case perhaps the hedgehogs become addicted to an easy meal and fail to eat enough natural food to make a balanced diet? Worse still, maybe they become so dependent upon food bowls being filled each evening that when folk go away or fail to put out food for other reasons, the hedgehogs suffer real distress? I've met people who arrange for 'hedgehog sitters' to take care of their hedgehogs when they go on holiday!

In order to investigate these ideas, my students and I carried out a radio-tracking study of hedgehogs that had already become accustomed to feeding at food bowls. The main study site was in the gardens adjacent to a golf course, the other site was my own garden. We made observations on up to five animals each evening, recording their positions and activity every 60 seconds for several hours at a stretch. We also watched their customary food bowl from dusk till midnight. Our observations were later fed into a computer which printed a map of where the hedgehogs had been and summarized their activity for the night. We set out to answer a series of specific questions:

*How close to the food bowl do the hedgehogs live?*
None of the food bowl 'regulars' lived in the garden where food had been put out for years (despite apparently suitable sites being available). One lived next door in the runner bean patch for a few days, another lived 50 metres away under a garden shed, but mostly the nest sites were over 100 metres distant. Two of the hedgehogs came in from over 500 metres away (a third of a mile), despite the fact there were plenty of other nest sites nearer the food. In fact one of these animals moved nearer the garden for a couple of days, then went back to its more remote nest. The one in the conveniently local bean patch moved too, but went to live in a thicket over three times further away from the food bowl. So hedgehogs don't appear to move into a cluster round the regular supply of food. Altogether, about 50 hedgehogs lived on the adjacent golf course within hedgehog walking distance of our study food bowl, but probably less than one third of them actually visit the bowl in a year.

*Do they wake up and make a 'bee line' for the food?*
If a food bowl was an irresistible magnet for hedgehogs, we would expect them to travel the shortest possible distance from the nest to the bowl and get there as soon as they could. In fact hardly any of the hedgehogs tried to do either. They often left the nest and set off in quite the wrong direction at first. At least half of them travelled more than twice as far as they need have done. One of them had journeyed over ¾ mile(1.2 km) before reaching the bowl, which was only 200 metres away by the shortest route. Mostly the hedgehogs took more than twice as long as they need have done to reach the food bowl. Several did not arrive for two or three hours when they could have done so in 15 minutes. Some nights they didn't bother to come at all and spent their time foraging on the golf course instead. Often the hedgehogs wasted 10 minutes or more (an hour and a half in one case) courting other hedgehogs, even though this was the end of the breeding season. A couple of the animals were prone to sitting about doing nothing for long periods, indifferent to the food which awaited them only a short distance away. In a couple of instances, hedgehogs travelled to the garden and then didn't bother to visit the bowl at all. The hedgehogs were certainly very variable in their behaviour; they obviously pleased themselves what they did and were not behaving like robots to fit our preconceived ideas of what they should do.

*Are hedgehogs 'faithful' to one garden?*
Now this is going to upset a lot of folk. In 17 nights, at least 11 different animals visited our principal food bowl. The six radio-tagged ones (all caught at that bowl) did not simply pop in off the golf course to feed at the special bowl and then go back again. They all went to other gardens as well. Sometimes, because of hedgehog-proof fences and walls, this necessitated a devious route in and out of garden gates and via secret hedgehog holes; but the normal pattern was to forage from one

garden to the next, taking in neighbours' food bowls on the way. So each particular garden does not have its own separate set of visitors. Moreover, on some nights the animals deserted the study garden and went to visit others in another road 200 metres away.

These observations answer another question too: it is obvious that hedgehogs do not stake out a territory and defend 'their' food bowl. They might fight off another animal that sought to feed at the same time, and timid hedgehogs clearly avoided competing with others. However, even our most active and dominant male hedgehog showed no sign whatever of trying to retain exclusive rights over the garden or its food bowl.

## How much bread and milk does a hedgehog eat?

We weighed the food bowl before and after each hedgehog had fed and we also noted the time it took to eat the weight of bread and milk removed. The largest amount guzzled in one go was 3.5oz (94g), over 10% of the hedgehog's body weight; equivalent to one of us eating 15lb or 7kg of porridge! Usually the animals ate only half that amount, but they often came back later for more. One slurped its way through 5.5oz (157g) during the course of an evening. Overall, the average rate of consumption was 7g (a quarter of an ounce) per minute spent at the bowl, so it is possible to time feeds with a watch and estimate the amount eaten by each animal by multiplying the number of minutes by 7g.

## Does this stop them eating enough natural food?

We can't answer this question properly because it depends what constitutes 'enough'. Nor have we yet got an accurate estimate of just how much natural food hedgehogs do eat in an hour or in an evening. However, we can be certain that none of our hedgehogs ate only bread

and milk. They might like it and eat lots of it, but they also spend a lot of time in normal foraging. This is precisely why they took so long to get to the food bowl and often didn't bother to come at all; they were busy picking up natural food, either on the golf course or around the gardens. After a big meal at the bowl, a hedgehog often sat still in the shrubbery for half an hour, no doubt burping gently, but always set about natural foraging again before going back to its nest. So they don't end up abandoning a natural diet in favour of living off bread and milk alone.

*What happens when the poor hedgehogs aren't fed?*
We tried the experiment of not putting food in the bowl for a few nights to see if the hedgehogs would just sit in the shrubbery waiting for food or go elsewhere. Reactions differed; some went to a neighbour's bowl, one charged about as though in disbelief (but the next night, took one sniff at the empty bowl and departed immediately). Another animal came back in hopes five times in one evening. None of them just sat waiting; all went and found other food.

We tried repeating these studies in my own garden, but for a much shorter time and on only three animals. The results were similar; none lived in the garden, they did not make a bee line for the food (even once they had reached the garden) or hurry themselves; all spent most of their time in natural foraging.

So it looks as though food bowls offer a welcome supplement to the hedgehog's diet, and are not the disruptive influence on sensible living that people often assume. Perhaps this isn't so surprising after all. Consider our own relationship with fish and chip shops. The food is warm, nutritious, cheap and plentiful; it's tasty too. We don't have the bother of washing up, nor do we have to cook the food ourselves. So why don't we all live next door to a chippy and eat there every night? And why isn't there widespread woe and hunger on Sundays when the chip shop is shut? Basically we don't behave like that, and nor do hedgehogs.

*Is bread and milk a suitable food for hedgehogs?*
There is not much published information about hedgehog milk. However, one analysis suggests that it is more concentrated than cow's

milk, containing twice as much protein and over twice the amount of fat. So cow's milk isn't as good as hedgehog milk, but some people go further than that and suggest that cow's milk is actually harmful to hedgehogs, making them ill and causing diarrhoea.

Is this true? It overlooks the fact that all mammals depend wholly on milk for the first few weeks of their life. True, that's milk from their mother, not a cow; but there is nothing actually poisonous in cow's milk. In fact it contains an excellent mixture of sugar, fat and protein: just what animals need. What harm is done by drinking it? Indeed some hedgehogs do so night after night, year after year, and travel considerable distances to get it.

The diarrhoea suffered by some animals may be caused by something quite different, but it is easy to settle this question by performing a simple series of experiments. It appears that if there is

# The problem with bread and milk: an experiment

We used four captive hedgehogs (3 females, 1 male) and fed them Pedigree Chum dog food diluted with crumbled dog biscuit, knowing this to be a good standard diet for hedgehogs. There was plenty of water for the animals to drink. On this diet, the hedgehog's droppings were all firm and dark brown in colour. We then fed them only on bread and milk for ten days, and this resulted in green sloppy droppings. Back on Chum for a week and all was well again. We then tried bread and water for a few days, biscuit and water, and finally biscuit and milk. Each experimental period was separated by a short time with Chum for food. The milk diets certainly caused diarrhoea and green droppings, but this was at least partly due to excess fluid in the diet because even water mixed with bread (or biscuit) caused the droppings to be rather loose.

The results were the same for all four animals and it is clear that bread and milk alone is not an ideal diet and does cause upset tummies. However, all four hedgehogs kept up a healthy body weight throughout the eight experimental weeks. Their weights dropped sharply over the weekends as they were not fed on Sundays, but recovered again the following week whether they were fed bread and milk or anything else.

too much cow's milk in the diet, hedgehogs will indeed 'get the runs'. Hence it is a good idea to ensure that the diet is varied and does not consist wholly of bread and milk. We know that wild hedgehogs do not exist solely on this unnatural food (see p. 119 and p. 120), and captive ones must be given a varied diet by offering table scraps, dog food and other things. Bread and milk is said to be fattening and, for this reason, should not be offered in large amounts to birds in the breeding season lest they stuff their nestlings with it and stunt their growth for lack of protein. However, for hedgehogs a fattening diet is exactly what they do need, especially in the autumn. They must have at least a quarter of their body weight stored as fat (the equivalent of 35lb/16kg for a full-grown man), and they have only a few weeks in which to acquire it. The fat will provide vital insulation and food (stored as fat) during hibernation.

In summer, hedgehogs (and many other ground-feeding animals) face the problem of drought. In periods of a week or more without rain, worms especially become hard to get and so do many other invertebrates; just at a time when many young hedgehogs are leaving the nest and trying to fend for themselves. Under such circumstances extra food and drink (of any kind) may mean the difference between life and death. The prolonged drought of 1976 made the ground so hard and dry that the hedgehog population in my local park was almost wiped out. Yet nearby garden hedgehogs were still numerous, thanks no doubt to extra food and drink put out in bowls.

Critics argue that, given bread and milk, hedgehogs will gorge themselves to the point of discomfort. Does that really matter, we sometimes do it ourselves! It is also said that the animals will fill up on bread and milk, which is a poor substitute for the natural food that they no longer feel it necessary to seek. But that is not what our studies of hedgehogs and food bowls showed, quite the opposite in fact. Where is the evidence that a bread and milk meal affects normal foraging behaviour? Our studies suggest that extra food of this sort does not significantly affect behaviour and merely serves as a useful addition to the natural food that is gathered during the rest of the night.

Exactly why bread and cow's milk upsets tummies is not clear. Almost certainly it is due to the special sugars that milk contains, not the fat or protein (so using skimmed milk doesn't help – the sugars are dissolved in the watery part of the milk). This is a serious problem for baby hedgehogs because diarrhoea not only drains them of energy, it also causes much water to be lost. They can easily die as a result. This is why it should not be fed to babies in captivity, but wild hedgehogs have plenty of other things in their to dilute the effects of the milk. One solution to the problem is to use goat's milk (or commercially available milk substitutes), but this is an expensive option and not always feasible. Another possibility is to dilute the milk with water, much as you might add soda to whisky. On its own, a cupful of whisky will do you no good at all, particularly on an empty stomach. But well-diluted, even a child could drink the stuff: though it should never be the only thing consumed! Exactly the same applies to hedgehogs and cow's milk. Other things are better for the animal, but watered down, milk will usually do more good than harm. However, baby hedgehogs shouldn't be encouraged to take too much of it, nor should they be given it in captivity. For captive hedgehogs it is much better to use an alternative diet such as dog food, biscuits and water for both adults and young, with as much added variety as possible.

Bread and milk is certainly not ideal fodder and should not be the major part of a hedgehog's diet. Nevertheless, it makes a valuable supplement to natural food. Many hedgehogs actually seem to prefer it to natural food and may often be seen guzzling bread and milk while slugs, which would normally be seized and eaten, feed alongside. In times of scarcity, finding such a dish must be very welcome indeed; perhaps even a salvation and certainly better than slow starvation. Putting out extra food, even bread and milk, is better than putting out nothing at all. Moreover, it could make all the difference to a nursing mother if she finds some extra moist food like this in dry weather. She needs extra food and drink to produce her own milk, and without enough moisture in her diet, her offspring may well die.

Perhaps the last word should come from the hedgehogs themselves as they vote with their feet. They come regularly for bread and milk, often travelling far to get it, and do so from one year to the next. They don't die from it. If bread and milk is bad for them, they are certainly gluttons for punishment. Nevertheless, it would be better to offer them something more nourishing and with fewer side effects, and to avoid giving it to babies or captive animals.

## Putting out food – keeping the scroungers at bay

Whilst people are happy to put out food for hedgehogs, they are dismayed to watch it being stolen by other animals. I am often asked if it is possible to prevent unwanted guests like cats, rats or magpies from taking advantage of a food bowl. The answer is 'yes' and it need not involve the use of a gun!

Tuck the food bowl under a dense bush or some other suitable cover, then make sure it can only be approached via a tunnel. Alternatively, construct a small cage from chicken wire (about 15"/ 40cm cube) to cover the bowl and fix it to the ground. The tunnel approach should be made from bricks, plastic, chicken wire or a concrete pipe. It should be big enough to allow the hedgehogs to get in, about 6" (15cm) diameter and at least 12"(30cm) long. A cat can get through a hole that size, but not a tunnel (because of its longer legs). If a small cat does manage it, lengthen the tunnel. A magpie will not fancy the tunnel at all and anyway will not feed at night, so put the food out after dark. Rats are more of a problem, but generally they are less interested in wet foods than dry materials. So long as the food put out is sloppy and wet they will be less attracted to it. Rats are likely to be attracted by bird food too, so if you have a bird table and don't have rat bother, then putting out food for hedgehogs should not create a new problem. If rats do cause trouble, then trapping them (in cage traps) may be the only answer.

# Marking and recognizing hedgehogs

With practice it is possible to recognize small differences in the shape, size and behaviour of individual hedgehogs. However, many of them do look very much the same, especially in the dark. Many people are convinced that they can recognize 'Winston, the big male' and other hoggy characters, but they may in fact be seeing more animals than they realize. The only way to be absolutely certain of individual identity is to mark the animals yourself. This will enable you to see how many hedgehogs visit your garden (usually more than you imagine); how often they come and how they behave towards each other. When I marked 'the hedgehog' that used to visit my garden, he turned out to be seven of them!

The best way to mark hedgehogs is to put paint on their spines, using either a brush or an aerosol spray can. Quick drying paint should be used to colour a patch about 1" (3 cm) in diameter, without matting the spines if possible and avoiding paint getting on to the hedgehog's skin or fur. White paint shows up best in torchlight; metallic touch-up paints for cars are quite suitable. You must avoid getting paint near the animal's face and ears. You can paint numbers on the hedgehogs, but they are often difficult to read. It is better to use patches set out in accordance with a pre-designed code. Imagine the animal divided into four quarters – right shoulder, left shoulder, right and left hip. Put one paint patch in each of these and you have four individually recognizable hedgehogs. Use pairs of patches in combination (e.g. right shoulder + right hip, left hip + right shoulder, etc.) and you have 10 individual patterns. The system can be extended to accommodate larger numbers if need be, by using up to four patches on one animal or adding a fifth rump patch like a cottontail rabbit (see chart).

Paint marks will remain visible for up to six months, sometimes longer. However, they get dirty and may need close inspection to be detected after a few weeks.

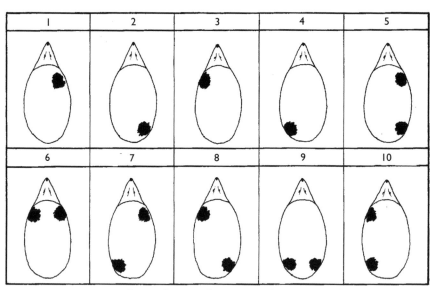

*Animal number and suggested paint marks*

| animal no | right shoulder | right hip | left shoulder | left hip | date 1st caught | sex | weight |
|---|---|---|---|---|---|---|---|
| 1 | X | | | | | | |
| 2 | | X | | | | | |
| 3 | | | X | | | | |
| 4 | | | | X | | | |
| 5 | X | X | | | | | |
| 6 | X | | X | | | | |
| 7 | X | | | X | | | |
| 8 | | X | X | | | | |
| 9 | | X | | X | | | |
| 10 | | | X | X | | | |

## A suggested marking code

*Copy this out and fill in the date, sex and weight of the animal marked with each pattern as you use it. Start at no.1 and work through the set of combinations. Note that this assumes a maximum of 2 paint patches on any one animal. The series can be extended beyond 10 by having up to 5 patches per animal.*

Use this scheme to recognize animals and give each a name or number. Once you have a population of marked animals you can begin some really interesting studies. First of all: how many hedgehogs come to your garden? Some people think they have 1 or 2 and in fact it's 8 or 10. You can check to see whether the bold ones or the slinky ones always behave that way or only when they are alone. How long do certain individuals continue to come regularly? Do young ones stay or disperse? How do hedgehogs behave towards one another? This is a key area of interest because little research has been done on the social behaviour of wild hedgehogs, so even an amateur study at home can contribute new information (provided the observations are systematic and careful). For example, some hedgehogs will drive others away from a food bowl; but is such dominance due to body size (big always dominant over small)? Are males dominant over females or does a hedgehog's position in the social hierarchy depend on something else? A study of the 'peck order' among hedgehogs would be most interesting. Marked animals can be watched to see who courts with whom, who fights or runs away, who feeds first at a bowl and who hangs back in the shrubbery.

If you clip patches of spines as well as using paint to mark them, your hedgehogs ought to be recognizable the following year. Then you can see whether it's the same ones that return, how long individuals might live and how many are marked and never seen again. In fact a lot of hedgehogs fall into this last category, suggesting that the hedgehog population may contain a large number of nomads. That's interesting for a start, but are these in fact young animals or the ones you have observed to be subordinate in the peck order? Maybe they are just being driven out by the resident hedgehogs?

Having marked animals come to your feeding bowl vastly increases the interest of watching them and hog watching on a dimly lit patio can be great fun. On most summer evenings it certainly beats watching television. A lady in Hertfordshire kindly sent me her hedgehog attendance register, covering 17 weeks of the summer from mid-May onwards. She marked the animals with different colours and wrote: 'I am amazed how many there are. In fact a sudden rush of new hedgehogs causes a paint crisis!' At least nine hedgehogs visited her food bowl. The register showed 'White' came consistently throughout

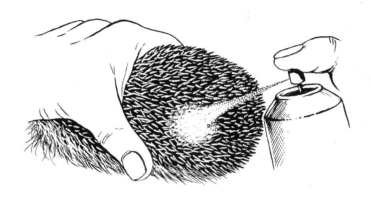

*Marking with spray paint – keep it away from the animal's face.*

the summer, although not every night; whereas 'Red Two', having discovered the food bowl in mid-July, hardly missed a single night thereafter. 'Yellow' was only ever seen twice. The periods of absence are particularly intriguing. Despite its regular attendance, 'White' would not be seen for intervals of up to 10 nights, even when food was available. 'Red One' came only 5 times in three months, with periods of 9, 12, 24 and 28 nights in between. 'Blue' was absent for up to 33 nights and 'Yellow Two' stayed away for 40 nights; all of which tends to suggest that the extra food put out for hedgehogs is very welcome but not dangerously addictive. Quite clearly the animals can manage without it and frequently do so of their own free choice (see also p. 119). If you have results from observing hedgehogs, please send them to the British Hedgehog Preservation Society (details on p. 203.)

# Slug pellets – are they a hazard to hedgehogs?

This is probably the question I am asked most often. It reflects a major and legitimate concern that people have for wildlife in their gardens, and their problem when trying to control damage done by slugs and snails. Because of its importance, I wrote to three of the biggest UK slug-pellet manufacturers asking some detailed questions. Two months later, I had not heard from one of them, another offered a bland assurance that there was nothing to worry about and they had never received any complaints. The third company offered some considered comment and referred to studies made in Switzerland by a Professor Schlatter, who seems to be the first person who looked at this problem specifically in relation to hedgehogs – and then got a lot of stick for doing so!

The most important 'active ingredient' of garden slug pellets is a substance called metaldehyde. The reason it is used against slugs is not because it is harmless to other things, but because slugs are killed by much smaller doses of it than are other creatures. The measurement of just how poisonous it is can never be really precise because some individual animals are more resistant than others. Environmental factors also interfere; for example, the effect of metaldehyde on slugs even depends on the weather. Nevertheless, slugs are killed at dose rates between 5 and 20 micrograms of metaldehyde per gram of slug; whereas dogs, guinea pigs and cats need 200-1,000 micrograms per gram – that's 40 to 50 times as much. In practice this means that eating, or even just contacting, a single pellet may be enough to kill a small slug; but a hedgehog sized animal, a cat or guinea pig would have to eat a lot more to kill it. That's the theory anyway, based on laboratory tests to discover how much poison, per gram of animal, it takes to kill 50% of the animals eating it. But do these laboratory tests, under artificial conditions, really provide a valid basis for assuming that our garden hedgehogs are not at risk? There are still some important, explicit questions that need answering:

*1. Will hedgehogs eat slug pellets?* Hedgehogs are omnivorous and will eat all sorts of stuff; however, they do not normally like hard dry things such as pellets, grain or stale bread. They normally prefer softer, moist food, though they will have a go at almost anything. In an effort to stop birds eating slug pellets, manufacturers incorporate a blue dye because birds have been found to peck at blue objects less often than any other colour. But this is unlikely to make much difference to a nocturnal hedgehog, who can't see colours in the dark. An unpleasant substance is also built into the pellets so that they taste and smell nasty, and this helps deter pets (and young children) from munching them in quantity. Nevertheless, since 1985 there have been plenty of post-mortem studies of hedgehogs confirming that they will and do eat slug pellets (perhaps after these have become softened by rain). It is likely that some hedgehogs will die as a result. A report of 74 hedgehog post mortem examinations, published in 1991, found that three contained traces of metaldehyde, but this does not prove that it was the cause of their deaths. However, residues in the liver of one showed that the poison had been absorbed, not just swallowed, and in sufficient quantity to be harmful. It is clear that hedgehogs can and do eat slug pellets and are in danger of being poisoned as a result.

*2. What if the hedgehogs eat the poisoned slugs?* Even if hedgehogs don't eat slug pellets, dead or sickly slugs would be easy prey for a foraging hedgehog who might readily find and consume a couple of dozen in a good night. The answer here centres on whether or not poisoned slugs have any residue of metaldehyde in or on them. We have done some experiments which suggest that metaldehyde soon decomposes inside dead slugs to form harmless chemicals. Nevertheless, if a poisoned slug did contain the whole dose that caused its death (perhaps 50 micrograms for a fairly big slug), a hedgehog would need to eat about 5,000 of these to take in the sort of dose that would kill a large guinea pig and therefore (presumably) a hedgehog.

*3. But don't small does of pesticides build up in the body?* With some insecticides (DDT for example), tiny residues accumulate in the body so that although an animal never takes in a lethal dose in one go, it may add small amounts for months or years until it has finally accumulated enough to kill it. However, metaldehyde does not build up in the body's tissues. Anyway, if dead slugs contain no residues that will harm the hedgehog there should be no problem.

4. *Can we be sure that results of toxicity tests using guinea pigs, rats, dogs and cats actually apply to hedgehogs too?* Hedgehogs may be more (or less?) sensitive than these laboratory animals; so can we generalize from one species to another? Here, we must turn to Professor Schlatter; he did test metaldehyde on hedgehogs and his results suggest that they have about the same sensitivity as cats and guinea pigs. He says it takes on average about 250 milligrams of metaldehyde to kill a 1lb(500g) hedgehog, far more than will be consumed by eating quite a lot of poisoned slugs or even a few actual pellets.

All this seems to give a green light to slug pellets, although some other studies carried out on the Continent suggest that poisoned slugs may indeed be dangerous to hedgehogs. However, this whole discussion relates to fatal doses of metaldehyde; we have not considered what effects smaller doses might have. Recent disasters in the chemical industry, fears over the widespread use of certain herbicides, and the complaints from people living near former chemical dumps all serve to show how serious sub-lethal doses of dangerous chemicals can be. Illness, dizziness, birth defects and sterility may be caused by almost immeasurably small amounts of harmful chemicals.

Nobody can be a hundred per cent confident about the safety of hedgehogs, although on the whole it does look as though slug pellets are not as dangerous as they might be. Nevertheless, the controversy as to whether or not slug pellets are harmful to hedgehogs has continued, encouraging various manufacturers to develop so-called 'safe' slug pellets. One product is available which is not a poisonous bait designed to be eaten, but acts by

drying up the slime-forming organs of slugs and snails that come into contact with it. It is also now possible to purchase some special parasitic worm eggs. These hatch into nematodes (eel worms) that specifically attack slugs. This form of biological control is expensive, but very specific, carrying no danger to unintended victims. It is too expensive to use over large areas, but ideal in small places like patios and greenhouses. Hopefully, further developments of this sort will ultimately make poisons obsolete and we will one day be able to rely on sophisticated biological methods of controlling garden pests and ban poisons altogether. Meanwhile, some people pin their hopes on using soot, ashes and various 'organic' slug control methods. Some of these may work some of the time, and they are unlikely to do much harm. But they are also unlikely to be as effective as poisons (especially not after heavy rain), so many people will continue to use conventional slug pellets.

All this relates to traditional metaldehyde-based slug pellets. Farmers use a different type, whose poisonous component is methiocarb. These pellets are distributed widely on the land and our experiments suggest that the poison does not break down and become harmless inside dead slugs. So, slugs poisoned on farms could be hazardous to hedgehogs (and other wildlife that eat them). The (slightly) good news is that a small study carried out in Germany suggests that slugs poisoned with methiocarb are rejected by hedgehogs, at least some of the time.

There is also the problem that pellets are visible and attract attention, but much garden and agricultural pest control involves the use of sprays. These substances are invisible after application and

**Requiem for a hedgehog**
It wasn't cars that killed him Or viruses or bugs. Oh no! You thoughtless gardeners, He ate YOUR POISONED SLUGS.

easily overlooked. Yet they are still poisonous and may wash off the vegetations and poison worms and other soil animals, creating another threat to wildlife – less obvious, but real just the same. The basic message from all this is that poisons kill things: that's what they are for. Once they are released into the environment we lose control over what they do and sometimes they will kill the wrong things. The best advice is to use poisons sparingly, only as directed on the packet, and try to avoid them altogether.

Finally you might remember just how often hedgehogs eat slugs and other garden pests. If, by careless use of garden chemicals, you kill or weaken your hedgehogs, your pests will rejoice, having fewer predators. You might then end up with a bigger problem than you started with.

# How to reduce the risk of hedgehogs (and other animals) eating slug pellets

1. Purchase only those that contain blue dye, to deter birds, and a substance to make them taste nasty to hedgehogs (the packet will sometimes say this).

2. Only put them out when and where you have a slug problem, not 'just in case'.

3. Lay them inside pieces of pipe or under a low tunnel made of bricks, where hedgehogs can't get at them. If you prop up a paving slab on small sticks or stones, to leave a 1-2cm gap underneath, this shady retreat will attract slugs. Put in some smelly bait like fresh orange peel and they will come from far and wide. Here you can leave slug pellets safely, as birds and hedgehogs cannot squeeze into such a small space and the slugs will be killed out of reach. The first night I tried this on my patio, no less than 25 slugs were dead by morning!

4. Remove or bury any dead slugs you find.

5. You should consider an alternative method of slug destruction (e.g slug traps baited with beer). You could also consider using an alternative chemical to kill slugs, but if the manufacturer has not tested it on hedgehogs, you are no better off than with conventional metaldehyde pellets and some of the alternatives are likely to be ineffective.

You could also think whether hedgehogs or lettuces are more important. You can buy the latter at any old greengrocers.

# Hibernation

Hibernation has attracted the interest of scientists from Aristotle onwards because it seems to be a form of 'living death'. How can normally warm-blooded animals go cold and apparently lifeless for weeks at a time and still not actually die? The 19th century anatomist John Hunter wrote several letters to his pupil Edward Jenner (a pioneer in medical vaccination) asking him to supply hedgehogs or to carry out experiments aimed at investigating the nature of hibernation. Hunter especially wanted to measure fat consumption over winter and body temperature in different regions of the animal. In the 20th century most of the laboratory studies done on hedgehogs focussed on the physiology of hibernation and what could be learned that might be useful in treating humans (see p. 177).

There are a lot of misconceptions about hibernation. It is usually assumed to be a kind of sleep: just deeper and longer lasting than usual. Actually it's much more complex than that, and the analogy with sleep is very misleading. Sleep is essential, hibernation is a variable and flexible adjustment to circumstances. Hibernation is not a kind of rest or recuperation; it's an energy conservation strategy. All animals need energy, which they get from food. It is used to grow, move about and live a normal active life. The hedgehog's fuel supply is in the form of worms, beetles and all the other things consumed in a night's foraging. In warm weather there is no problem, but as the weather gets colder, the invertebrates on which hedgehogs feed become scarcer and more difficult to find. If it's not careful a hedgehog may use up more energy looking for food than it can get from eating what it finds. Insectivorous birds face this problem too and many of them respond by flying away to warmer places where food is still abundant. The hedgehog can't do this and adopts the alternative strategy of becoming inactive and using as little energy as possible until the weather and food supplies improve.

One of the most energy-expensive activities is keeping the body warm, especially for poorly insulated hedgehogs. So, to save energy, they abandon the attempt: the body furnaces are allowed to burn out and the hedgehog's temperature falls from about 35°C to 10°C or

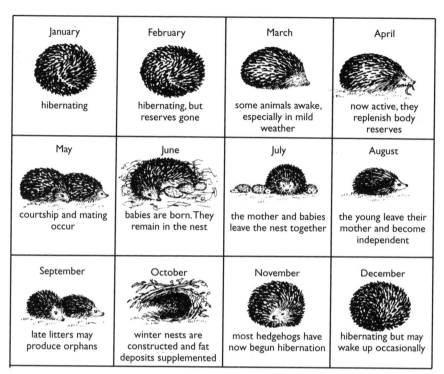

| January | February | March | April |
|---|---|---|---|
| hibernating | hibernating, but reserves gone | some animals awake, especially in mild weather | now active, they replenish body reserves |

| May | June | July | August |
|---|---|---|---|
| courtship and mating occur | babies are born. They remain in the nest | the mother and babies leave the nest together | the young leave their mother and become independent |

| September | October | November | December |
|---|---|---|---|
| late litters may produce orphans | winter nests are constructed and fat deposits supplemented | most hedgehogs have now begun hibernation | hibernating but may wake up occasionally |

*The hedgehog year*

less to match its surroundings. In very cold conditions, the metabolic engines are stoked up gently so as to ensure that the body does not cool below 1°C and risk frostbite or freezing solid. Allowing the body to cool saves a lot of energy, but in consequence all the chemical reactions associated with normal activities like nerve conduction, digestion, growth, breathing and movement are slowed right down almost to a standstill. The heart rate slows to less than 20 beats per minute; respiration almost stops altogether and up to an hour may elapse between short bursts of breathing. These changes economize further on energy expenditure, but at the price of complete immobility and major changes in the chemistry of the body that cannot be swiftly reversed. Nevertheless, energy consumption in hibernation is reduced by over 90%, the hedgehog's way of overcoming the problem of food shortage in winter.

So, faced with insufficient food/energy to maintain normal levels

of its bodily activities, the hedgehog responds by giving up normal activity and shutting down energy consumption to the barest minimum needed to stay alive (about 2% of normal requirements). This is hibernation.

Once you can understand how hibernation serves to save energy during the winter shortage of food, several worrying questions begin to answer themselves. For example, if there is plenty of food about despite it being winter, there is no need to hibernate and many hedgehogs may remain active well into November and December in good years. In the warmer climate of New Zealand, hibernation is necessary for only a brief few weeks in mid-winter, whereas in Scandinavia the winters are longer and so hibernation is prolonged. A period of bad weather in spring or autumn may again reduce food availability to the point where inactivity and fasting is more efficient than trying to maintain normal activity; so again hibernation may occur even though it is not winter. Hibernation is thus a flexible strategy that can be adjusted to meet different circumstances.

Perhaps you can also see why a hibernating hedgehog should not be kept warm? Higher temperatures (e.g. 20°C) raise the rate at which chemical reactions take place in the body and this uses up precious energy which can't be replaced without full arousal and going out to feed. Once the hedgehog has become inactive and started to hibernate, its body temperature needs to be as low as possible (a minimum of 1°C) to slow its metabolism and the rate at which energy is used up. This is why 'keeping hedgehogs warm' over winter is not a good idea.

During hibernation the hedgehog is torpid and incapable of feeding. Its fuel supply comes from the masses of fat stored below the skin and inside its body. This is 'white fat', like you get on bacon, and at the beginning of hibernation may comprise one third of the total body weight. This precious store is gently used up over the course of the winter. In addition, there are large orange coloured lobes around the shoulders, below the skin. These form the so-called 'brown fat'. Its special purpose is to generate heat when the animal wants to warm up and resume normal activity: fuel for the furnaces. It follows that, before it hibernates, the hedgehog must have accumulated enough white fat to last it for many weeks and enough brown fat to enable it to successfully wake up several times – otherwise hibernation will simply be a prelude to death (as it is in many young and underfed animals). So it is vital that hedgehogs get enough to eat in the weeks before hibernation not only to live and grow but also to store as fat to last the winter. Any baby or undersized hedgehog that hibernates at a body weight less than about 1lb (450g) has too little fat on board

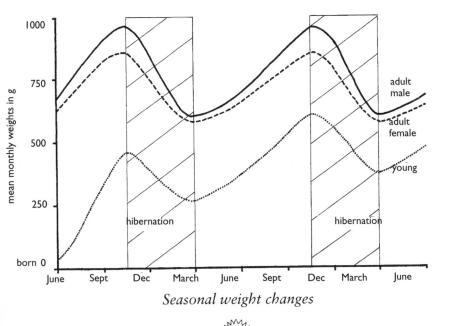

*Seasonal weight changes*

to survive more than the briefest period of winter. Some authors have claimed that hedgehogs need to weigh 1lb 7oz (600g) or more to survive the winter. Obviously, the fitter they are the better. In Britain 1lb(450g) is the minimum, below which they will not survive; 1lb 7oz may well be an *optimum* figure ensuring a higher probability of not dying, but it is not the *minimum* size necessary. To use this higher figure as a threshold results in many more animals being 'rescued' and brought into captivity than is really necessary. My estimates are based on analysing samples of hedgehogs at the end of winter and assuming that about 20-25% of body weight was lost as fat reserves were used up (a realistic figure based on several other studies of hibernators). From this it appears that the smallest animals found alive at the end of winter must have been more than 1lb (450g) the previous autumn. Those that were smaller than this, reduced by 20+% are simply not present among spring samples of hedgehogs, so they must have died. A study in Denmark, based on recapturing radio-tagged animals over winter, suggests that about 1lb 2oz (512g) is the minimum weight needed for survival, but Danish winters may last a bit longer than British ones.

It is generally assumed that hibernation is continuous – that all being well, the hedgehog goes to sleep about Guy Fawkes' day and wakes up at Easter. In fact arousal is both normal and fairly frequent.

On average, hedgehogs wake up about once a week, although some may not do so for three or four months. Arousal involves raising the body temperature from perhaps 5°C to 30°C or more and this usually takes at least 3-4 hours. The hedgehog then spends a day or two in a fairly normal state before sinking back into hibernation. During this time the hedgehog may leave its nest and go for a walk, but this is comparatively rare. This periodic wakefulness happens quite spontaneously, although of course hedgehogs will also be aroused by disturbance, flooding and even unseasonably warm sunshine. Although the majority of these arousal periods are passed inside the nest, hedgehogs will normally come out and change their winter nest at least once. It is rare for an animal to spend the whole winter in the same nest and new ones will be built during mild nights.

# Baby hedgehogs in the autumn

Is it cruel to take them indoors or should they be left alone? If they have insufficient fat reserves by October, indicated by a body weight of less than 1lb (450g), leaving small hedgehogs alone is to condemn them to almost certain death. Indoors they can be properly fed and will remain fully active, provided that they can be given plenty of food and are not exposed to temperatures lower than about 10°C. They can then grow to a 'safe' size and be released at any time during good weather to build a winter nest and hibernate. Or, they can be kept indoors, fully fed and active all winter and be released all the better for it next spring. Note that this only really applies to babies found after about mid-September or early October. Earlier in the summer they ought to be able to fend for themselves and are probably better off left to do so.

# Winter nesting

There have been many studies made on hedgehogs in the laboratory (particularly by researchers in Scandinavia) to investigate the physiological details of hibernation, but hardly anything is known about hibernation habits in the wild. To remedy this, I studied the hedgehogs in a West London park for six winters, recording when and where the nests (hibernacula) were built, how often they were used and how long they lasted. As the autumn nights got colder, the hedgehogs stopped using the main grassy areas of the park and began to congregate inside small (supposedly rabbit proof) fenced-off areas of brambles and scrub. Here they built their winter nests, tucked up against fallen logs or underneath bramble strands or piles of brushwood. Elsewhere they use similar sites and also go under sheds and even down rabbit holes to spend the winter.

There were always more nests than hedgehogs, almost as though each one built himself a spare hibernaculum in case it was needed later. Yet if a hedgehog did change nests in the middle of the winter (most did so at

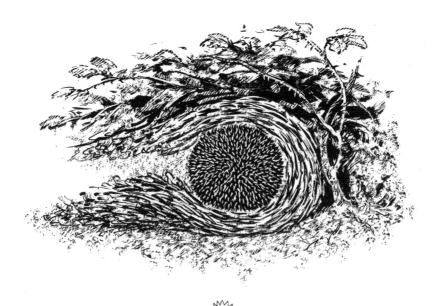

least once), it always built a new one and never moved into a ready made nest. Some nests were small and soon fell to pieces. These were probably made by young animals; building good nests needs practice. Only young ones ever shared nests and then not for long; wild hedgehogs hibernate alone. Curiously they do the opposite in captivity and often insist on sharing nest boxes when others nearby remain empty.

A typical hibernation nest is a bulky structure about 20"(50cm) in diameter, built on the ground and mostly made of leaves. Often grass, bracken and other materials are used, but leaves are best because they are more weatherproof. The hedgehog gathers them, a few at a time, and carries them in its mouth back to the chosen site. It then makes a pile, thrusting each new batch into the centre of the heap. When it has enough, the hedgehog burrows inside and begins to shuffle round and round. Normally this would simply cause the leaves to become scattered, but the site is chosen well so that the pile of leaves is held together by the support of adjacent logs or brambles. The shuffling action causes all the leaves to become similarly orientated and packed flat against each other, like the pages of a book. The nest ends up as a small chamber, entered by a short tunnel and with walls made of a wad of flat-packed leaves up to 4"(10cm) thick. This type of nest will last well over a year, but those built one winter are never used the next winter, even when they are still available. However, other things such as bees, wasps and wood mice eagerly take them over.

The leafy hibernacula are not only very weatherproof but also provide excellent insulation against the cold (and also inconveniently warm days). In fact the nest walls are so effective that for more than three quarters of the time, the inside of the nest is kept between 1°C and 5°C, even when the air temperature falls to -8° or rises above +10°. Laboratory studies show that the hedgehog's hibernation is most efficient at conserving energy if the body is kept at 4°C. So the nest, the hedgehog's only protection in winter, is also playing its part in ensuring the success of the hibernation strategy by keeping it at the right temperature. The winter nest is so important for the success and survival of hedgehogs that the availability of suitable nest sites and building materials may be one of the major factors that determine hedgehog distribution. Perhaps this is why they are scarce on moorland and in pine woods and marshland (see p. 19), rather than shortage of food, as is often imagined. These are the very habitats in which dry leaves are difficult to get in sufficient quantity to build a nest. Similarly, across Northern Europe, the hedgehog is rarely found beyond the limits of deciduous trees: not because it's too cold or there is no food, but simply because no trees means no leaves and no protective winter nest.

# Is it harmful for a hedgehog not to hibernate?

No. Whereas it certainly is harmful to do without sleep, hibernation is optional. Provided there is enough food available and the air temperature is not too low (less than about 8°C), there is no need for a hedgehog to hibernate, so it won't. This particularly applies to hedgehogs kept indoors over winter, but also to those that are well fed in the comparative warmth of urban areas. These may hibernate later. When overwintered captives are let go in the spring, they are well fed and have a distinct advantage over wild ones whose reserves are depleted by hibernation. If kept indoors, they show no ill effects, and may go on to breed perfectly normally.

## Hedgehogs, hibernation and climate change
Future climate changes may alter the pattern of hedgehog behaviour. Perhaps Britain will become more like New Zealand, allowing longer breeding seasons and reducing the time spent in hibernation? In fact the nature of climate change is hard to predict, and so are the effects. Will we get more rain, warmer nights, warmer winters, windier days? Who knows.

Meanwhile, there is no shortage of speculation, especially in the media, often by ill informed reporters. Once a story gets into print it obtains a legitimacy that often secures its acceptance without necessarily being subjected to critical analysis. When the perils of global warming became a fashionable source of discussion, there were high profile stories about a few hedgehogs being seen in February, interpreted as clear evidence that winters were already getting warmer and that doom was upon us. November 1994 was the mildest since records began, a clear 3°C above average apparently, and sure enough there were tales on TV about large numbers of hedgehogs being seen active instead of in hibernation. Again this was assumed to be harmful and it was asserted that the animals would be at risk later having not hibernated at 'the proper time'. Sundry 'experts', happy to court publicity, pronounced that there was something afoot. But no evidence in support of these ideas was ever advanced. Reporters who telephoned me were reluctant to accept that there was no story here because, to them, it seemed there must be.

In fact, winter activity by hedgehogs is perfectly normal and in this case I had published relevant information over a quarter of a century earlier! An analysis of 992 sightings and hedgehog road casualties in London showed that hedgehogs were active throughout the year. No less than 11.3% of the total records were from November and December. Many of the late autumn sightings were of juveniles, presumably attempting to fatten up for hibernation, even as late as Christmas Day. Far from being harmful to feed late, it is a good idea, provided that they can find food. They need to build up maximum fat reserves in case the winter lasts longer than usual.

As for activity in February, 32 animals were recorded in the three coldest months of the year, January to March inclusive. These observations were obtained by members of the London Natural History Society between 1956 and 1964, long before the widespread concern about global warming. The data files for the Atlas of British Mammals (published in 1993), also show approximately 6% of 1,688 road casualty records came from after late October, with a few more from January and February.

Winter activity is not freakish at all. In fact, laboratory studies show that hibernating hedgehogs arouse regularly during hibernation,

*Sledgehog*

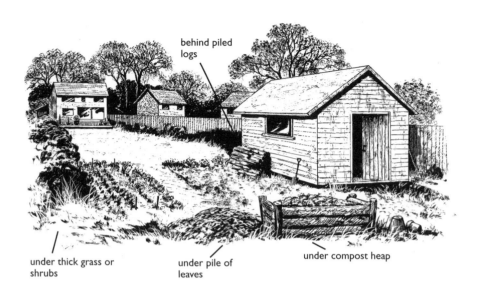

behind piled logs

under thick grass or shrubs

under pile of leaves

under compost heap

*Good hibernation sites in a typical garden. Anywhere that a pile of leaves may form and remain undisturbed over winter is suitable; there is no need to build a special hedgehog house if dry secluded nooks are already available.*

about every 7-8 days, even when the temperature is held constant. In the wild, my studies of hedgehogs using winter nests, over 6 successive winters (in the 1960s) showed that 60% of hibernacula were occupied for two months or less. Only two nests in a sample of 167 were occupied continuously throughout an entire winter. Thus, hedgehogs normally wake up sometime over winter and build a new nest or move to an existing one, often several times.

The idea that winter activity is peculiar or dangerous stems from misunderstanding the nature of hibernation. Hedgehogs do not hibernate on a particular date because 'it is time to go'. Instead they do so in order to resolve the dilemma that being warm blooded costs energy, but food energy becomes increasingly hard to get as the weather worsens in the autumn. It's a flexible behaviour and likely to adjust to whatever the climatic circumstances require.

It is a pity that reporters don't check their facts more carefully before spreading misconceptions and confusing ideas. It is also a shame that

# Hibernation – a variable feast

Many published statements relating to the 'hibernation period' of the hedgehog convey the impression that hibernation starts and ends on relatively consistent dates. But hibernation is not that simple. Mild weather delays hibernation and young animals (particularly those born in late litters) may anyway remain fully active into December. Adult hedgehogs will meanwhile have begun to hibernate, with males doing so earlier than females. Males would have several months since the peak of the breeding season in which to fatten up and by September their average body weight is already over 2lb (900g)(females average 3oz /100g less). They are fully prepared for hibernation quite early in the autumn. By contrast, females have a strenuous time producing at least one litter, giving them little opportunity to build up fat reserves. Females who have had late litters may still be producing milk (thus actually losing fat), so they are not ready to enter hibernation until after the adult males.

So, age, sex and the weather all influence the timing of these events and climatic differences between different regions of the country also modify the hibernation cycle, making generalisations inappropriate for the country as a whole. I analysed over 1,700 dated records from different parts of Britain, assuming that the number of hedgehogs recorded by observers represented a rough indication of the active hedgehog population. This showed clearly that hedgehogs emerged from hibernation earlier in the mild south-west than elsewhere. Whereas 42% of the year's hedgehogs had been seen by June in south-west England, only 34% had been recorded by then in London and just 32% in East Anglia. It was a further month before Scotland's hedgehog population achieved a comparable level of activity.

New Zealand hedgehogs experience mild, almost subtropical conditions, especially in North Island. If sightings data are rearranged to permit comparison with the British information, it is evident that 36% of the year's hedgehogs are recorded by June (actually December in New Zealand); a figure which lies between that for south-west England and London. The mild winters also seem to result in more activity during late winter. This may be because, at latitude 40°S (Southern England is 51°N), hedgehogs hardly need to hibernate at all.

'experts' do not urge caution and a more critical examination of stories that are aired from time to time. However since these shortcomings are likely to persist, it is worth taking time to consider the following questions when a 'news' story breaks:

1. Is this likely?
2. What is the evidence, what are the facts as opposed to assertions?
3. How many observations were made; is this just a 'one off'?
4. Is this story really significant or just another case of media hype and gullibility?

Now apply this analysis to the newspaper stories in 2005 that the increased popularity of 'decking' in suburban gardens was a likely cause of hedgehog extinction ...

# Population size and density: how many hedgehogs are there?

This question is almost impossible to answer. The problem lies with counting methods. Big animals, like deer, visible in daylight, can be counted just by looking at them, perhaps aided by binoculars. But hedgehogs are nocturnal and hard to see in the dark, even out in the open; who knows how many more of them lurk under bushes and in long grass and dense woodland?

Biologists often use 'mark and recapture' methods to census animal populations. A sample of animals is caught, marked and released. Later another sample is caught, and from the proportion of marked to unmarked animals in the second sample an estimate is made of total population size. It's fine with beetles and even mice, but not hedgehogs. You can't catch big enough samples at once, nor be sure that your catching method is not itself interfering with the population. People can mark the hedgehogs that visit their gardens. Suppose that 10 animals show up in the course of a month. Does that mean that every garden has 10 hedgehogs? How many of those 10 are also part of the 10 that visit someone else's garden? What about the ones that were marked and never seen again – are they dead or have they merely gone somewhere else? It's hard to say.

It has been suggested that hedgehogs live at a density of about 1 per acre (2.5 per hectare). If the area of England is 50,000 square miles, then the English population of hedgehogs numbers about 32 million – or so the argument runs. But if the original estimate of 1 per acre was based upon seeing about 30 hedgehogs during an evening stroll through 30 acres of parkland (with plenty of scope for counting some animals twice and no allowance for family groups increasing the total) then the 'count' could be highly misleading. On a different evening's stroll, perhaps only 10 hedgehogs would be seen in the same area; especially if the night was cool. Of course it is also misleading to assume that the population density in one place or habitat (a park in this instance) is the same as would be found in central Birmingham or on the Pennine Way. An estimate of 32 million English hedgehogs could easily be wrong by the odd 25 million animals!

Radio-tracking studies (see p. 72) show that an average hedgehog's home range might be about 50 acres (20 hectares), but it does not defend this patch as an exclusive territory; other hedgehogs share it too. Thus you can't say each hedgehog needs 50 acres, therefore England has 50,000 square miles divided by 50 acres = 640,000 hedgehogs.

The best we can do for the moment is to refer to an area that has been studied in detail. This is a West London golf course of about 100 acres (40 ha.) on which the permanent hedgehog population, according to different census methods, was about 30 animals three years running. This is an average density of very roughly 1 per hectare (2.4 acres). We (and others) have found similar numbers in other good hedgehog places. My student Alison Tutt tried three different methods of population estimation on Alderney and again got estimates of about one hedgehog per hectare. However it would be rash to use this figure to estimate the total British (or even English) population, because the countryside varies so much. More studies are needed to estimate population densities in different habitats, but they will not be easy to carry out. Allowing for the fact that plenty of places aren't good for hedgehogs, the total British hedgehog population could be about 1.5 million, but I wouldn't bet on it.

# Are hedgehogs increasing or declining in numbers?

Until we can find some way of making an accurate hedgehog census, this question can never be answered with precision. Since it is so difficult to estimate the size of hedgehog populations at one time, it is hopeless to compare estimates made at different times to check for increase or decrease. The fact that we normally see hedgehogs in twos and threes rather than dozens adds to the problem. Suppose one week you have three hedgehogs visiting the garden; if a fourth appears the next week that's a thirty per cent increase in numbers of hedgehog visitors. But it hardly represents a thirty per cent population explosion.

# The 1990 WI survey

One of the most frequent questions asked about hedgehogs is, 'Are they getting rarer?" Although it is difficult to answer this scientifically, we can at least collect a wide range of opinions, through the use of questionnaires. This we did in 1990, distributing thousands of forms with the help of the National Federation of Women's Institutes. Members of the WI returned over 1,200 forms, giving an indication of the regional abundance of hedgehogs and people's perceptions of them. There was clear agreement nationally that hedgehogs were certainly not getting more common. The number of people who thought that hedgehogs were decreasing roughly matched those who thought numbers remained the same, but there were statistically significant differences between regions. People in the Midlands and northern England felt hedgehogs were more common than those in southern England and Wales (this is similar to the results obtained by counting road casualties in different parts of Britain, see p. 150). Few thought they were more abundant.

As expected, hedgehogs were very popular, liked by 98% of those who returned questionnaires. Most of the 14 respondents who did not like hedgehogs gave fleas as the reason, although two people didn't like their prickles. Garden hedgehogs were fed by one third of those replying to our questions, mostly providing bread and milk, but also cat and dog foods. While many people were aware that slug pellets may be dangerous to wildlife, 48.7% of those with gardens still used them.

## Evidence of decline

Usually people ask about a decline in numbers because they have seen so many dead hedgehogs squashed on the roads. But dead hedgehogs may be a good sign as well as a bad one; a point discussed elsewhere. Perhaps we could use numbers killed on the roads as an indication of hedgehog abundance from year to year? In an attempt to find out, I organized lots of volunteers to fill in forms when they travelled about each summer, recording miles driven and hedgehogs seen. That way we can calculate a figure for hedgehogs seen per 100 miles that might show whether a decline is in progress. I have been severely castigated for initiating such an 'unscientific' study, partly because so many other factors (e.g. traffic density) may affect the numbers seen.

Maybe, but if we don't even try to collect information, who can say what it might mean? Road kills do not reflect traffic density; there are far more killed in New Zealand than in Britain, where traffic density is much higher. Meanwhile, for three years (1990-1992 inclusive), numbers killed on British roads showed a surprising consistency. Death rates were higher in North East England than in the South East or South West (despite higher traffic density in the South East). This pattern was consistent from year to year, and similar to the regional pattern shown by numbers of hedgehogs killed by gamekeepers. This consistency suggests the information might be reliable after all.

My colleague Paul Bright repeated these summer counts ten years later as part of the national *Mammals on Roads Survey*. Volunteers collected details of road casualties on 625,000 miles of roads. They showed a consistent and statistically significant decline in numbers per 100 miles of roads in the years 2001-2004 inclusive, with numbers down by 20% in just four years. Hedgehog road deaths averaged about 3 per 62 miles of road driven in Scotland, compared with only 1.5-2 per 62 miles in England and Wales. Numbers had also fallen by 30% compared to my counts of ten years earlier. So, it's official – hedgehogs are getting much scarcer than they were, and the decline continues.

Gamekeepers provide further evidence that populations are diminishing (see p. 154), especially in eastern England, although it's not clear why that should be. Probably the best explanation is that certain changes in the countryside must reduce their numbers. For example, at the time of the First World War there were several million horses on British farms. These were replaced by vehicles, and their pastures were turned into crop growing areas. Conversion to arable farming continued throughout the 20th century, turning grazing land into crops, particularly cereals. Small, closely grazed pastures, with plenty of dung heaps, provide ideal feeding sites for hedgehogs, with adjacent copses and hedgerows in which to nest. Conversely, arable land, treated with umpteen chemicals to remove the very 'pests' that hedgehogs need for food, is almost a hedgehog desert. Fields were also progressively enlarged to accommodate bigger tractors, taking out the hedges needed for nest sites. Radio tracking suggests that hedgehogs make little use of arable fields.

These changes occurred over very big areas of our countryside in the past 50 years or so and must have resulted in far fewer hedgehogs. On the other hand, expansion of towns was probably less of a threat to hedgehogs than to most animals. Food and nest sites abound in suburbia where hedgehogs are safe from gamekeepers and farmers. Nevertheless, urban infill, replacing large houses and their gardens by building lots of tiny houses and neat gardens, has probably meant fewer hedgehogs in towns too. New threats like road traffic, pesticides and mowing machines add to the hedgehog's problems.

There can be no question that hedgehogs are less numerous now than in the recent past and their decline seems likely to continue as remaining isolated populations die out. Hardly anyone I speak to thinks that hedgehogs are as common as before and most people tell me the same thing – that they haven't seen one for ages. In 2004 I gave a lecture to the RSPB group in Croydon (south London), an area with abundant hedgehogs in the 1960s. I asked the audience of 120 people how many had seen a hedgehog in their garden that year. Only two had done so.

These worrying trends, revealed through the observations of hundreds of caring volunteers, had to be seriously considered and in 2007 the hedgehog was added to Britain's official Biodiversity Action Plan. This lists species whose status is cause for concern. Hedgehogs are still quite numerous in some places, but for how much longer? Something needs to be done and it is not appropriate to simply brush aside this species as 'common and widespread' any more. That same year, my friend and colleague Dilys Breese died. It was she who had made one of the BBC's most popular wildlife TV programmes called *The Great Hedgehog Mystery*. When it was first broadcast in the early 1980s, it was seen by over 12 million people, a figure that far exceeds current viewing numbers. Dilys had gained a soft spot for hedgehogs and left a substantial sum to help them in her will. This makes it possible for the People's Trust for Endangered Species and the British Hedgehog Preservation Society to support a big campaign of research and practical hedgehog-helping. This is a fine way to do something helpful in the afterlife and I hope the hedgehogs will be suitably grateful.

# Persecution by gamekeepers

There is no doubt that hedgehogs do occasionally eat the eggs and chicks of ground-nesting birds (including gulls, terns and waders, see p. 65) and in parts of Britain where pheasants and partridges are highly regarded such depredations constitute a capital offence! So hedgehogs and other suspected nest robbers are exterminated with an almost crusading enthusiasm. On just one estate in East Anglia, nearly 20,000 hedgehogs were killed in the early 20th century, including 780 in a single year. Yet after 50 years an annual toll of 300 or so was still possible; there was no sign that the hedgehog was becoming extinct. The keepers said that they had managed to eradicate hedgehogs over the main part of the estate and they were simply killing immigrants that came in from surrounding farms each year. This may have been true to some extent, but many of their 'new' animals were in fact quite old, suggesting that they had escaped death for several years.

Gamekeepers see 'vermin control' as an important aspect of their jobs and, in the past anyway, have been encouraged in their destructive vendettas by the payment of a bounty for every predator killed. The usual reward for a hedgehog snout or tail was about three pence; a useful source of pocket money for the gamekeeper. Nowadays, British gamekeepers are fewer in number and too busy with all sorts of other work to bother much about hedgehogs; but even so at least 5,000 hedgehogs are probably killed by them each year in this country. Legal protection for the hedgehog (see p. 174) may have reduced this number somewhat, but the gamekeeper remains one of the hedgehog's few persistent predators.

But are hedgehogs really

WHAT DID I DO?

so much of a threat to the gamekeepers' interests? The hedgehog's diet does include eggs (see p. 65), but not often. Back in the 1930s a study was made of partridge nests to see who were the major predators responsible for the destruction of over 1,200 clutches of eggs. Hedgehogs accounted for only 1.3%; foxes took 34% and were obviously the principal culprits. Moreover, cats and dogs destroyed more of the nests than did hedgehogs and nearly a third of the partridge clutches were lost because of careless farm workers driving farm machinery over them. So, if gamekeepers really want to protect partridges, they would be better off shooting farm workers not hedgehogs! Another study, this time of pheasant nests, showed that crows and foxes accounted for three-quarters of predation; hedgehogs were only very minor culprits.

For a gamekeeper to go out deliberately trying to catch hedgehogs just to prevent a 2% loss of eggs is clearly a silly way to waste time. But actually the keepers normally do not trap specifically for hedgehogs. They set traps primarily to catch rats, weasels and stoats and simply kill hedgehogs as a kind of by-product of this activity. Nevertheless, it cannot really be cost-effective. If a keeper wants 100 more pheasants, the easiest way to get them is to buy some eggs from a bulk supplier and hatch them in an incubator, not go around trying to stop hedgehogs taking birds from his stock. Modern gamekeepers are more enlightened than their forebears and nowadays do not really constitute a serious threat to the survival of hedgehogs. Indeed if we look at the changing distribution and abundance of gamekeepers over the past hundred years, it seems that they might be heading for extinction sooner than hedgehogs.

In 1992, Stephen Tapper, one of my former students, produced a fascinating book (*Game Heritage*, published by The Game Conservancy, Fordingbridge, Hants). This reviewed the numbers of game birds and 'vermin' killed each year on sporting estates over the previous three decades. Although gamekeepers and bag records are an imperfect way of monitoring the fortunes of our wildlife, for many species it's the only system we have. How much better it would be if we had the money to maintain regular surveys of mammals the way it's done for birds! Anyway, the figures for hedgehogs killed by gamekeepers show a clear downward trend from about 2 or 3 per square kilometre in the 1960s to less than 1 in the 1980s. This could mean that gamekeepers nowadays make less effort to kill them, or it could be further evidence of a real decline in hedgehog numbers. One interesting point is that numbers killed per square kilometre are highest in the north-east of England and lowest in the south-west, an intriguing correspondence with the prevalence of road casualties (see p. 147).

# Do gamekeepers provide evidence of population cycles in hedgehogs?

Many big country estates keep a record of how many hedgehogs and other 'vermin' are killed on their land each year. Sometimes these records go back for decades. Some biologists have attempted to plot the numbers on graph paper to see if there are regular peaks and troughs in the totals which might suggest that hedgehog populations undergo regular cycles, with abnormally large numbers every four or seven years for example. The trouble with this sort of exercise is that you can't be sure that the trapping effort has remained constant; usually it hasn't. During the wars for example, many gamekeepers were away killing real enemies instead of hedgehogs, so 'lows' in say 1916 or 1943 are meaningless. Similarly, higher numbers may be killed one year simply because an extra gamekeeper had been put on the payroll.

If you look at the numbers that gamekeepers kill each month, there is further evidence that the figures reveal 'gamekeeper effort' as much as hedgehog population size. There is often a persecution peak in May-June. One estate I visited killed large numbers in June and I protested that this was the wrong time; to eradicate hedgehogs the effort to kill them should be made before breeding not afterwards. The old gamekeeper listened to this sagely and said, 'Ah, but it's in June the varmints do the damage.' Apparently if he discovered hedgehogs any other time of the year, when clearing brushwood in the autumn for example, he would gently move them to a safer place!

*Why did the hedgehog cross the road? To see its flat mate.*

*Why did the hedgehog cross the road? To show he had guts.*

# Lifespan and survival

The first four weeks of a hedgehog's life are quite likely to be its last because nearly a fifth of baby hedgehogs succumb even before becoming independent of their mothers. Once they have left the nest and struck out on their own, young hedgehogs are very dependent upon getting plenty of food. In dry or cold summers, this can be difficult and lead to further mortality; but in a normal year they feed well and grow steadily to reach a weight of perhaps 1¼lb(600g) before it is time to hibernate in October/November. Those born early in the summer have plenty of time to do this; late-born young face serious problems (see p. 89). The next big hurdle is hibernation. Much depends upon the length and severity of winter and what fat reserves the animal was able to accumulate before winter began.

The vicissitudes of early life are such that over half of all the hedgehogs that leave their mother's nest may never see their first birthday. But having survived that long, things start to look up, and

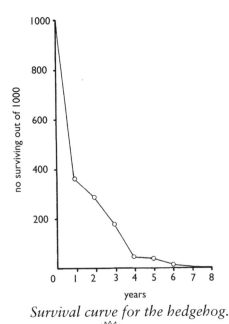

*Survival curve for the hedgehog.*

the chances of surviving the next winter increase. Hedgehogs have few predators and old age doesn't begin for at least four or five years. Whereas about one third of young hedgehogs survive into the following year, among adults the survival rate is double that; two thirds of the adults alive this year will probably be around next year too. Much depends on the weather and food supplies. There are also increasing threats from road traffic and mowing machines. Studies in Scandinavia, using mark and recapture methods, suggest similar survival rates among adults and young to those I have given here, which are based on counting growth lines in jaws. Once a hedgehog has left its mother's nest its average life expectancy is about two years. Four hedgehogs in a thousand might reach seven years old and one in ten thousand could live to be ten. It must be rare indeed for any hedgehog to live longer than that, if only because its teeth get worn out as a result of eating gritty food.

# Telling the age of hedgehogs

There is no easy way of doing this, especially with live animals. Big ones are likely to be older, but size is so variable that some one-year-olds can be nearly twice the weight of others three years their senior. Some hedgehogs 'look old', but who's to know whether they are or not? The only way to be sure is to use one of the rather specialized laboratory techniques employed by biologists. In the hedgehog I found that bones (especially the lower jaw) develop 'growth lines' as they get bigger, just like growth rings in a tree. The bone grows during the summer as the hedgehog is active and well fed, but in winter hibernation shuts down the processes of bone growth, interrupting its formation. By collecting jaws from dead hedgehogs and cutting thin sections of them, these alternate bands of growth and winter resting can be studied under the microscope. The number of growth lines indicates the animal's age. In turn, this allows estimates of survival from one age group to the next, as I have given on p. 156.

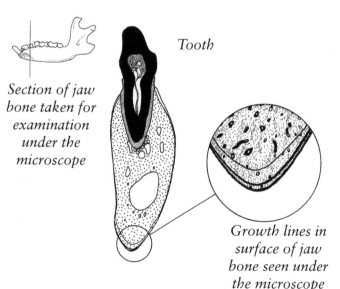

*Tooth*

*Section of jaw bone taken for examination under the microscope*

*Growth lines in surface of jaw bone seen under the microscope*

# Hedgehogs and badgers

Hedgehogs are sufficiently well protected by their spines that most predators leave them alone. The exception seems to be the badger. This animal has claws long enough to reach the skin between the hedgehog's spines and its forepaws are strong enough to rip open even the most resistant victim. Whilst badgers remained fairly uncommon, they represented only a minor threat to hedgehog numbers. This is no longer the case. The British badger population was estimated at about a quarter of a million in the late 1980s, but numbers increased by at least 10% during the 1990s, with an extra 25,000 badgers by 2004. The problem is that badgers not only kill hedgehogs and eat them, but they also eat similar foods to hedgehogs. The same worm cannot be eaten by both. So if badger numbers increase, there will be less food for hedgehogs (and many other creatures, including birds). Badgers are big animals and each one eats about the same amount as seven hedgehogs, so for every extra badger, there can be seven fewer hogs. This is a bit simplistic, but the principle is sound. An extra

*Badger gingerly investigating hedgehog*

25,000 badgers must result in at least 100,000 fewer hedgehogs, and the other quarter of a million badgers are a serious obstacle to hedgehog survival and success.

Following studies of hedgehogs in Oxfordshire and the numbers killed there by badgers, researchers at Oxford University predicted the absence of hedgehogs from areas where badger density exceeds 2.27 setts per 10 square kilometres. The implication of such a prediction is for a marked decline in hedgehog populations in certain regions of Britain. The National Badger Survey, carried out between 1985 and 1988, included an estimate of sett density per square kilometre for 10 regions (see **below**), making it possible to see where the problem might be most acute.

| Region | Average no of active badger setts per 10 sq km | Badger density per 10 sq km |
|---|---|---|
| North England | 0.96 | 5.664 |
| North West England | 1.49 | 8.791 |
| Yorkshire and Humberside | 1.08 | 6.372 |
| West Midlands | 2.77* | 16.343 |
| East Midlands | 1.7 | 10.03 |
| East Anglia | 1.52 | 8.968 |
| South West England | 4.51* | 26.609 |
| South East England | 3.22* | 18.998 |
| Wales | 2.88* | 16.992 |
| Scotland | 0.56 | 3.304 |

*Badger sett density per 10 square kilometres and numbers of badgers, based on The National Badger Survey of 1985-1988. This estimated the average number of badgers in a social group as 5.9 and is assumed to be the number of badgers per sett. Badger density is presented here as per 10 square kilometres for comparison with the Oxfordshire study. The figures marked by * represent those areas where hedgehogs might be seriously affected by badger density – West Midlands, South West England, South East England and Wales. Since the 1980s badger numbers have increased significantly.*

If the predictions are correct, in the four regions where badger numbers already exceed 13 per 10 square kilometres, hedgehogs may be in danger of extinction. Badger numbers have increased substantially since those figures were calculated and the threat is now almost universal. There is no escaping the conclusion that infinite numbers of both hedgehogs and badgers cannot coexist, not only because one preys upon the other but because much of their diet is very similar. The same food can't be eaten both! More badgers must mean less hedgehogs. This is perhaps something we should think about when considering hedgehog conservation.

I am not blaming badgers, any more than I blame hedgehogs for eating birds' eggs, it's just what they do. Nor do I dislike badgers, and still recall the thrill of seeing them for the first time over 40 years ago. But they were scarce in those days and they aren't now. The implications for hedgehog survival are serious. It's hard to know what, if anything, can be done to help. But ignoring the issue or pretending that badgers exist only by harmless drinking of rainwater doesn't help at all.

# Causes of death

For most hedgehogs, the biggest threat to their continued survival is hibernation. At that time they are defenceless against floods, cold, disturbance and wrecking of their nests. All the time they are using up their precious and irreplaceable stores of fat which, depending on the weather, may or may not run out before foraging becomes profitable again in the spring. Apart from these physical and physiological problems of hibernation, the hedgehog has little to fear. Whereas many small mammals run a serious risk every day of becoming food for some predator, adult hedgehogs are almost immune to attack except from badgers (see p. 159). Polecats, even tawny owls occasionally have a go at the odd hedgehog, but they stand little chance of killing it except in the case of very young animals whose spines are thin and whose skin and rolling-up muscles are not fully developed. Bits of hedgehog are quite common in the stomachs and droppings of town-dwelling foxes, but most likely this is a result of scavenging squashed carcasses off the roads rather than deliberate killing. Foxes are supposed to push rolled-up hedgehogs into water and kill them when they uncurl. Even supposing that a fox would go to so much trouble, killing the hedgehog would still not be an easy job. Gamekeepers (see p. 152) and motor cars (see p. 165) kill some too; others die from disease, poisoning (see p. 163)and getting caught up in netting or plastic litter. About half the hedgehogs brought into animal care centres suffer from problems due to natural causes (parasites, abandonment of young, attacks by dogs, etc). The others suffer from new threats created by humans (poisoning, injury from cars, mowing machines and litter, for example). This suggests that these new dangers, to which the hedgehog has had no time to evolve a defence, are now a serious threat to hedgehog numbers.

Although hedgehogs are comparatively safe from enemies, they seem to be very accident-prone. They are especially good at falling into things. Perhaps this is because the cushioning effect of their spines (see p. 29) means that they do not fear falling. Anyway they fall into holes, building site trenches, rubbish pits, swimming pools and garden ponds (see p. 111) everywhere. They get caught in cattle grids too; I heard of one where 52 had died. A campaign was started in Scotland to persuade local authorities to build ramps or escape tunnels into cattle grids so that careless hedgehogs could get out. The British Hedgehog Preservation Society did the same in England and Wales, with much publicity and greater effect. Doubtless these escape routes will also mean a second lease of life for countless toads, newts, small mammals, beetles and lesser forms of life that might otherwise end up starved to death in the bottom of a cattle grid along with the hedgehogs.

If hedgehogs fall into cattle grids, then perhaps they also go down suburban drains? Many of these have a grille in the gutter with an adjacent hole in the kerb about 12" x 6" (30cm x 15cm), easily big enough to admit an inquisitive hedgehog bent on exploring the roadside. Many could die this way, although nobody has investigated whether they do or not.

Hedgehogs are at some risk from what they eat as they take a bite at almost anything within reach, some of which could be harmful to them. Very important is the fact that the things they eat most often (slugs, caterpillars, beetles, etc.) are the very things that farmers and gardeners try to kill with pesticides. It is likely that much of the hedgehog's natural food becomes contaminated with small amounts of such poisons (at least in the recent past). One beetle may contain a minute amount of pesticide for example, but the hedgehog might eat 20 of them in an hour, hundreds in a week, progressively accumulating more and more toxic substances in its own body. We know from studies on birds that organochlorine pesticides (such as DDT, Aldrin and Dieldrin), which are specially intended for use on the sort of things hedgehogs eat, are not easily eliminated from the body. Toxic residues of these substances build up slowly in the liver and in fat. Hedgehogs depend very much on fat to tide them over the winter and by accumulating pesticide-contaminated fat during the summer a hedgehog may be sowing the seeds of its own destruction when the fat is used up during hibernation. Other new chemicals, often used to control pests, are based on synthetic hormones. Their effects on hedgehogs are unknown, although fish and fresh water creatures can be seriously affected. Anyway, whatever methods are used to control 'pests' will reduce the food available to hedgehogs if they are successful.

No studies have been made of hedgehogs and pesticides, although

*Ramp to escape from cattle grid*

some investigations of bats (which also feed on invertebrates and store fat for hibernation) have shown that they are very seriously threatened by pesticide contamination of their prey. The good news is that these dangerous cumulative pesticides have now been banned for more than ten years and their effects will gradually fade. However, hedgehogs were probably badly affected for several decades and meanwhile new chemicals threaten similar problems. For example, PCBs, used in various industrial processes, are cumulative and cause sterility in animals at incredibly low doses. These chemicals are now widespread pollutants, despite rigorous controls on their use and disposal.

Hedgehogs are also susceptible to accidents that are not their fault. Many of them must die when gardeners burn piles of garden refuse, complete with the hedgehogs that have burrowed in to hibernate in peace over winter. To avoid doing this, make your bonfire in a spot adjacent to your pile of debris, and then move stuff across in order to burn it. This way you will spot any hibernating hedgehogs and also any other wildlife that is sheltering there. Hedgehogs also risk death through doing silly things, like the one seen in somebody's garage licking the acid encrustations off an old car battery.

Others probably get mown in the summer when long grass is cut. Certainly hedgehogs with patches of chewed-up spines are not uncommon. Several times each summer tractors tow big gang mowers and swipes along road verges to cut the grass. Our radio tracking shows that, in warm weather especially, many hedgehogs spend their days asleep in such places. The mowers will cause them serious, perhaps fatal, injuries, but we are unaware of this because few people walk the verges and the bits of body will be buried in grass cuttings or soon eaten by scavengers. A similar threat is posed by strimmers, the mowing machines with a whirling cord at the end of a long pole. These are used a lot to manage course vegetation, again the sort of places that hedgehogs lie up in. Strimmers do appalling damage to hedgehogs, chopping off legs, noses and scalping the body indiscriminately. In the last 20 years or so strimmer victims have become one of the most numerous wildlife casualties brought into animal hospitals. Many others suffer a painful death. I know rank vegetation needs to be kept under control, but be careful! If you use a strimmer, feel about with your foot first time to make sure there isn't a helpless hedgehog asleep among the leaves and plant debris that you are about to assault.

# Road deaths

Sadly, most of us are more likely to see hedgehogs as squashed remains on the road than as live animals amiably trundling about their business. Sometimes it is very disturbing to return from a journey by car with a distinct impression of having seen lots of dead hedgehogs; but probably because their corpses are large and distinctive, we are just more conscious of them than we are of dead rats for example. The spiny skin is surprisingly resistant to repeated battering by vehicle tyres (it may even strike back on thin tyres as cyclists know to their cost). When pounded into the road, the skin remains visible and recognizable for longer than the thin soft skin of rabbits and other mammals. This helps to exaggerate the apparent abundance of road-death hedgehogs. On a car journey you may see dead rabbits and hedgehogs, but the rabbits are likely to have been killed in the preceding few days, whereas some of the hedgehogs will have been there for weeks.

When surveys have been carried out to discover which species are killed on the roads most often, the poor old hedgehog usually comes in the top four mammal species (along with rabbit, squirrel and brown rat). It is impossible to know how many hedgehogs are killed on our roads each year, but the total must be many thousands.

In Denmark, a country about a third the size of England, surveys suggest about 70,000-100,000 hedgehogs are run over annually (out of a total of about 10 million vertebrate animals killed), although that is not a recent figure. Nobody has attempted an overall estimate for Britain based on anything other than guesswork, but one estimate, originally published in a Sunday newspaper in the 1960s, suggested that a million British hedgehogs might die this way each year. That figure was certainly wrong, but it has often been quoted since. A study 50 years ago in Hampshire recorded 112 hedgehogs on roads in 2 years, an average of between 1 and 2 per 100 miles examined during the summer months. Another study totted up 756 hedgehogs on Yorkshire roads in 5.5 years. The problem is how to scale this up in proportion to the total length of road in Britain. If you get the scaling up factor wrong, or the original sample was too small to be reliable, you come up with silly numbers – like a million.

The *Mammals on Roads Survey* of 2001-2004 offers some more recent and more reliable information. In those four years 6,411 dead hedgehogs were counted on a total of 270,000 miles of roads. That's an average of about one hedgehog per 42 miles of road. Since there are 245,000 miles of similar roads in Britain, one might estimate an annual mortality of about 5,900 animals, but the surveys only covered three months (July-September) each year. So, scaling this up to take account of hedgehogs being active for at least six months of the year, the annual mortality seems likely to be at least 12,000 animals and perhaps 15,000. This excludes any killed on motorways, but how often *are* hedgehogs killed on motorways? My impression is that it's rather few, perhaps because motorways are so wide and inhospitable that hedgehogs turn back rather than cross them. Alternatively I may simply be driving too fast to notice their corpses. Anyway, it seems likely that about 15,000 hedgehogs die on our roads each year.

Naturally, all these dead hedgehogs cause considerable concern. Surely if the carnage continues, hedgehogs will soon become rare or even extinct, or so say the pessimists anyway? I would prefer to look on the brighter side and observe that hedgehogs aren't extinct, despite all the road deaths, and that just shows what a successful creature the hedgehog is. It survives in spite of all this destruction. The slaughter on the roads is cause for optimism and faith in the hedgehog's resilience; not evidence of its imminent doom. It's a pity just the same that so many are killed in this way, and alarming that numbers seem to be declining.

Despite the numbers killed, roads probably don't represent a really major threat to hedgehogs overall. For example, of the 80 or so hedgehogs marked in one of our study areas we only found a couple of them killed on nearby roads, even though local traffic was very dense and very fast. A similar study in New Zealand, again in an area of relatively high traffic density, found only 4% of marked hedgehogs ended up squashed on the road. If our annual death toll really is about 15,000, then it's only 1% of the total population (assuming there really are 1.5 million hogs altogether ...). Nevertheless, vehicles are a form of predator to which the hedgehog is not adapted, so this represents an addition to natural mortality rates.

Squashed hedgehogs are one of the main subjects that people talk to me about, and it is very interesting to see how interpretations differ. One sort of comment will be along the lines of, 'Hedgehogs must be getting common, I've seen so many more killed on the roads this year.' Another version of this is, 'I've seen so many hedgehogs dead this year there can't be many left; they must be getting scarce.' The same observation, but two completely different interpretations. I have heard the same two lines of argument in relation to the numbers of badgers seen dead on roads over the past 40 years. Badger road deaths are certainly more numerous nowadays. I recently counted 6 dead in 100 miles, whereas 30 years ago I would have been surprised to see any all year. The key point is that independent counts of badger setts and actual numbers of live badgers confirm that badgers have greatly increased in numbers, so increased numbers of road casualties genuinely reflect a real increase in population size. Another study has shown that the number of rabbits killed on roads was closely linked to actual numbers seen alive on surrounding land. So, roadkills probably do represent a reasonable index of hedgehog abundance, reflecting changes in relative numbers from year to year. Counting them is therefore a worthwhile exercise.

*Roadhog*

I also hear a third sort of comment to the effect that, 'I've seen fewer squashed hedgehogs this year,' referring to the same year that other people claim to have seen *more* dead animals. It serves to underline the problems of trying to estimate hedgehog numbers and suggests that we can't learn anything very useful from a study of road casualty figures without plenty of different observers, all following a similar counting method (as in the *Mammals on Roads Survey* for example). We may also learn something else. If you travel the same route regularly and note where hedgehogs occur, there do seem to be 'accident black spots' where animals are often seen dead; yet for long distances in either direction there are few if any road casualties. Could this be evidence that hedgehogs have regularly used trails and tend to use the same crossing points when attempting to get across the road? If so, maybe it would be possible to create small fences to dissuade them from going on to the road?

Driving about we also become aware that hedgehogs are often killed near buildings and in suburban areas; fewer are seen out in open country. This is part of the evidence suggesting that hedgehog populations in some habitats (especially towns) are denser than elsewhere. Similar evidence indicates that hedgehog populations in parts of New Zealand may be denser than in Britain. There are simply more animals killed on a given length of road there than here. And if more are killed, there must be more available to be killed ...

Let us accept the assumption that the number of dead hedgehogs is a reflection of the number of live ones. In other words, when there are more hedgehogs out and about, more will end up dead on the roads. Carrying this assumption further, we can compare numbers seen at different times of the year. One interesting observation is that larger numbers are killed in April-May than in June. It has been suggested that this is due to young, inexperienced, babies leaving the nest and getting run over soon after. But this can't really be the explanation because few babies leave the nest before July. Anyway the squashed hedgehogs early in the year are practically all adults. It's more likely that the peak numbers of road deaths are a reflection of greater hedgehog activity in the breeding season; more chasing about seeking mates, for example. This is especially likely to be the real explanation because about two thirds of springtime road casualties are males and our radio tracking confirms that males move about much more than females.

*The sex ratio in samples of hedgehogs collected from roads varies with the time of year.*

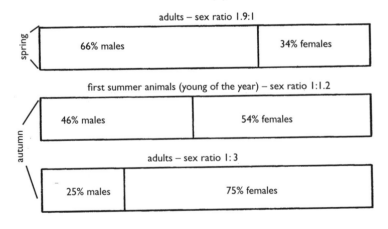

adults – sex ratio 1.9:1

| spring | 66% males | 34% females |

first summer animals (young of the year) – sex ratio 1:1.2

| autumn | 46% males | 54% females |

adults – sex ratio 1:3

| 25% males | 75% females |

# Running hedgehogs: evolution in action?

The reason that the hedgehog comes a cropper so often is of course due to the animal's natural reaction to danger. If attacked, it rolls up; excellent protection against predators but no defence in the face of 10-ton lorries. Some years ago, a theory was given wide publicity that hedgehogs may be evolving into a new form that runs away from oncoming traffic instead of rolling up and staying put. The idea had a convincing air of Darwinian natural selection: 'survival of the fittest', although there wasn't a shred of evidence in support of it. Hedgehogs that rolled up when threatened by approaching vehicles got squashed and eliminated from the population. Those that ran away instead lived to see another day and pass on their 'running' genes to the next generation of hedgehogs. Thus, the theory ran, we are witnessing the evolution of a new race: the fleet-of-foot hedgehog. The idea has a convincing simplicity about it, although there is no way of testing it because we can't compare the behaviour of modern hedgehogs with their behaviour in the years before cars were invented. The main trouble

with the theory is that it is based on a false assumption: that running away increases the probability of escape. It doesn't (see diagram). Running could, in some circumstances, be more dangerous not less. The only way that running could really help is if the hedgehog could run faster than the approaching vehicle. This can't happen often even though some hedgehogs can travel quite fast and some drivers move extraordinarily slowly.

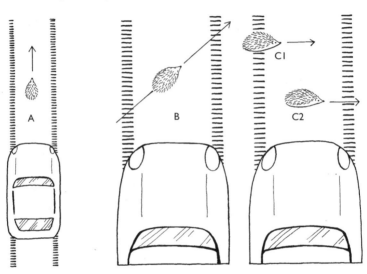

*A. If the hedgehog runs in the same direction as the car, it is either still in or still out of the path of the wheels, the same as if it sat still. Running doesn't increase its chance of survival.*
*B. If the hedgehog runs, but obliquely across the path of the car it actually spends longer in the wheel tracks through crossing them at an angle. Running therefore make it more likely to be killed, not less.*
*C 1. The only way running will help escape is if the animal is already in the wheel track and it runs at right angles to the car's path, getting it out of the way. But it mustn't run under the other wheel, and is best off doing a U turn, which takes longer and therefore still involves the risk of being run over.*
*C 2. If the hedgehog is in the path of the car, but not actually in the track of the wheels, it is better off staying still. To run means going into the path of a wheel and risking death.*

In short, running doesn't guarantee survival, nor even improve the chance of it. Yet this idea, despite its central weakness and lack of evidence, has been extraordinarily persistent. I still get asked about it 30 years after it was first aired in a newspaper, then on the radio. In 1995 this unsupported theory was given a boost to its credibility by being adopted as the basis for a real GCSE science exam question, still without any evidence.

# Hedgehogs and the law

In 1566, in the reign of Queen Elizabeth I, a law was passed for the 'Preservation of Grayne'. This listed various animals (like rats and mice) that were thought to be responsible for damage to agricultural interests, declared them to be vermin and put a price on their heads to encourage wholesale destruction. For some reason, the hedgehog was fingered as a villain and it was decreed that payment of three pence should be made for every hedgehog killed throughout the realm. Churchwardens were charged with the duty of paying out this money for all the hedgehogs and other vermin slaughtered within their parish. They did so, and meticulously recorded these bounty payments in the parish records.

Today, in county record offices, it is possible to inspect the old churchwardens' accounts, painstakingly inscribed with quill pens in big ledgers, recording the fates of thousands of hedgehogs in bygone years. Sometimes the records continue for decades, reflecting diligent persecution. In other places, the killing of hedgehogs was more desultory. Where a long series of records exist, we can plot the number killed per year on a graph and sometimes get a result that looks like evidence of population cycles in the hedgehog. However, we should not jump to hasty conclusions for the same reason that applies to the interpretation of gamekeeper's records (see p. 155): we do not know for sure that the effort put into catching hedgehogs was the same from year to year. Far from having cycles of abundance, the hedgehog population might have been stable and the fluctuations in numbers killed recorded by churchwardens may only reflect different levels of blood-thirstiness in successive generations of parishioners. An even more likely cause for these annual variations would be the periodic rediscovery by impecunious little boys that their local churchwarden was a useful source of extra pocket money to be gained at the expense of a few hapless hedgehogs.

It is clear that nobody went all-out to eradicate hedgehogs, despite bounty payments. Indeed, with the benefit of hindsight, we can see today that bounty payments are an ineffective method of pest control.

Modern experience with foxes, squirrels and other animals with an official price on their heads suggests that the 'vermin' often end up more abundant than before and country folk treat their vermin populations not as pests, but as a valuable economic resource.

Bounty payments certainly don't seem to have caused the extinction of hedgehogs, but when I first learned of them I thought it would be amusing to take a couple of dead hedgehogs to my local parish officials and demand the payment due to me under that statute of Elizabeth I. However, I quickly discovered that the law in question had been repealed in 1863, along with a whole batch of other obsolete and useless legislation; the hedgehog is officially blameless once again.

Nevertheless, for 300 years the hedgehog was, by Act of Parliament, a statutory pest. Ironically, it is today, also by law, a protected animal. The Wildlife and Countryside Act of 1981 sought to harmonize British legislation with that of other European countries. The hedgehog is not one of the mammals given absolute protection (like the otter for example), but is listed in Schedule 6 along with certain other animals that may not be captured or killed by certain methods without a licence. Another list explains what the 'certain methods' are. Literally interpreted, our countryside legislation makes it illegal to kill hedgehogs using a machine-gun. Also, more inconveniently, it is now technically illegal for anyone to catch hedgehogs at night using a torch, without an official government licence that you are supposed to carry with you at all times, available for inspection by a constable. Clearly this wasn't really the intention of the Act, but that's how it comes out on paper. Laws ought to mean what they say and they ought to be obeyed; but in this case literal interpretation borders on the farcical. Hedgehogs may not be trapped either, except under special licence, and this creates a problem for gamekeepers who often catch hedgehogs as a by-product of trapping for something else. It is unclear whether a gamekeeper could be successfully prosecuted for trapping a hedgehog 'accidentally', but one effect of this is to reduce the numbers of dead hedgehogs reported by gamekeepers, perhaps giving a false impression that fewer are killed now than before 1981.

The first Queen Elizabeth declared hedgehogs to be vermin, but the second Queen Elizabeth has now made them a protected species. History may reveal that neither made much difference. The evidence for hedgehogs really being vermin is as debatable as the need for present-day legal protection. Modern hedgehogs are not seriously threatened by the sort of things the law now seeks to stop, but by changes in land use that are not affected by this protective legislation. The main reason why hedgehogs are on the list of protected species is probably that this brings Britain into line with some other European countries where, as a matter of principle, animals are protected automatically unless they are actually a pest. Legal protection will not save hedgehogs from being squashed on the roads, nor will it eliminate the effects of garden chemicals, ploughing up pastureland or careless use of strimmers and mowing machines, all of which are serious threats that reduce hedgehog numbers to a greater extent than the activities prevented by law.

A further problem is that the 1981 legislation protected hedgehogs from non-existent dangers (like being machine gunned or caught through the use of a tape recorder), but failed to protect them from deliberate cruelty. Attempts to prosecute vandals for beating and burning hedgehogs have failed in the past because anti-cruelty legislation did not extend to wildlife, covering only pets and captive animals. The hedgehog is a special case that needs attention here. Unlike most mammals, hedgehogs can be easily caught by hand. They are then the passive victims of whatever sadistic and bestial behaviour their captors choose to inflict on them. Campaigns to get hedgehogs protected from cruel mistreatment failed to move Parliament in 1991, despite lengthy petitions and much public support, but in 1996 Parliament passed the Wild Mammals (Protection) Act, in which the hedgehog was a major beneficiary. It is now illegal, under penalty of imprisonment or a £5,000 fine, to treat a wild hedgehog in a cruel manner by beating, burning, kicking, impaling, stoning, nailing, crushing or drowning it. That should cover most eventualities, but the problem now is to catch offenders and prove that their actions were cruel. For example, some youths were prosecuted for kicking a rolled-up hedgehog in the road, as though it was a football. They claimed it was dead already. But was it actually alive and suffering illegal mistreatment or was it a road casualty and their behaviour was no more than brutish and distasteful? How can a policeman be sure if he did not observe the full incident and was only called out after the event?

# The uses of hedgehogs

One of the best known uses for hedgehogs is as croquet balls by Alice in Wonderland. Alice had a lot of bother with them getting stuck in furrows. They also kept running away; although these difficulties were nothing compared to using flamingos as the mallets, with all the players fighting to get at the hedgehogs at once and the Red Queen rapidly losing her temper with the whole game.

The other well known (perhaps more practical) use for hedgehogs is as a tasty meal. In the past at least, gypsies dined off them regularly and particularly favoured animals caught in the autumn when they were very fat and juicy before hibernation. The traditional recipe called for a large dollop of clay with which to encase the hedgehog. It would then be roasted in the embers of a hot fire for an hour or two and when the clay covering was cracked off the spines would be removed too, embedded in it. I have never tried this, for the same reason that I expect most modern gypsies haven't either. Moreover, I suspect that corned beef in tins is both more convenient and more attractive than hedgehog in clay. I also saw a story reported in a wartime issue of *The Naturalist* that a German gipsy had been fined heavily for trying to eat a hedgehog without the appropriate ration card!

Back in the Middle Ages, many animals (including some quite repulsive ones) were believed to be useful for medicinal purposes. The hedgehog was no exception and in 1658 the Reverend Topsel listed in his *History of Four Footed Beasts and Serpents* some of the ways in

*Alice's use of hedgehogs*

which potions containing bits of hedgehog were supposed to alleviate human ailments. For example, the dried rib skin, mixed with pepper and laurel leaves, cast into 3 cups of warm water, was recommended for 'one that hath the colick'. Hedgehog ashes (!) were good for boils and the powdered skin would stop your hair falling out. Using burning hedgehog as a fumigant, 'by God's help', would cure urinary stones. The hedgehog's right eye, fried in linseed oil and drunk from a brass vessel, would improve night vision; and its fat 'stayeth the flux of the bowels'. Today we might have more confidence in other remedies, but Topsel was only repeating what earlier authors had asserted and he did not record contemporary endorsement or scepticism.

One amusing quirk is that Topsel suggested the use of hedgehogs to cure leprosy. This is rubbish of course, but hedgehogs have indeed been used for that purpose, although not in a way that Topsel might have foreseen. It turns out that hedgehogs (and armadillos) are, for some reason, very susceptible to leprosy and so could make ideal animals to use in laboratory studies aimed at seeking a cure for this disease. Armadillos are not easy to get in large numbers (especially outside America), and so hedgehogs may be used as a laboratory tool in this area of medical research.

Another quite different area of medical research has a hedgehog dimension. Studies on these and other relevant animals have shown that during hibernation the body tissues are much more tolerant of trauma than is normally the case. Moreover, at reduced body temperatures, body tissues need less oxygen. These principles are put to use during major surgery, when operations on humans are carried out at artificially low body temperatures. Maybe if we understood more about the natural mechanisms of hibernation, we could go further and do without anaesthetics; or consider operations that might last for days; or 'hibernate' sick people so that they don't get any worse while they wait their turn for an operation or hospital bed? It has also been suggested that if we could find a way to make people capable of hibernating like the hedgehog, so that they would use no food and little oxygen for months at a time, it would greatly ease the problems of long-duration space travel in necessarily small space capsules. A return trip to another planet for example might take a couple of very boring years. In that time an astronaut would need a

*Carding wool using dried spiny skins*

very large store of food (and get pretty fed up with it). Much better to hibernate for 6 months or so. Moreover, studies on hibernating animals suggest that they might be, to some extent, less susceptible to the damaging effects of radiation: another potentially valuable asset in space travel.

There are plenty of more prosaic uses for hedgehogs, or at least their spines. If the spiny part of the skin is stretched flat and allowed to dry hard, it forms a durable pad of sharp spikes like a bed of fine nails. In bygone days this formed the basis for the tools used for 'carding' wool and dressing flax, combing the fibres out till they lie parallel with each other as a necessary preparation for spinning into threads. A similar dried, bristly hedgehog skin made a good (if rather fierce) brush for fluffing up woollen garments and combing out tangles in woollen cloth. On a live hedgehog, the spines will yield fairly freely if you touch them, but in a dried skin they are fixed rigidly. A mass of such spines is a potential hazard, worse than a barbed wire carpet, and an effective deterrent to casual contact. Small wonder that in days gone by, farmers would nail hedgehog skins to the top rails of their orchard gates to keep out small boys. It is also said that nineteenth-century coachmen attached hedgehog skins to strategic parts of their carriage shafts to prevent their horses from dozing on the job. If the weary horse leant to one side for a snooze in the shafts, it got an uncomfortable jab in the haunches to keep it awake.

There are now lots of products inspired by hedgehogs, ranging from shopping bags to notepaper and board games. One company makes boot wipers shaped like hedgehogs, the stiff bristles being ideal for scraping off mud from wellies.

# Hedgehogs in folklore

One of the oldest stories about hedgehogs must be the one about carrying fruit on their spines. This activity was described by Topsel in his *History of Four Footed Beasts and Serpents* and is mentioned in almost all the English accounts of hedgehogs published in the 300 years since then. Topsel probably got the tale from the works of the Roman author Pliny who had written down a mixture of fact and fable he gleaned 2,000 years ago. Basically the story is that hedgehogs use their prickles to impale fruit and then carry it off to their nests. The fetching and carrying of apples by this means is convincingly illustrated in several mediaeval books. Sometimes the tale is embellished by having the hedgehogs climb a tree first and cast themselves down on to fruit lying below. Normally the objects of attention are described as apples, but occasionally grapes and other soft fruits are mentioned; especially in old accounts from France and Spain where such fruit might be easier for hedgehogs to find. The story is not just a European yarn, but is also told as far away as China. But is it true?

You can certainly demonstrate for yourself that the hedgehog can carry fruit on its back. If you impale a squashy apple on to a patch of spines and jiggle it about, the animal will contract muscles that cause the spines to bristle. This helps to hold the fruit firmly enough to stay

*A medieval illustration of hedgehogs collecting fruit*

in place when the animal walks away. The problem is to understand how a hedgehog could get the fruit stuck there for itself. The old stories say that hedgehogs roll on the apples, but even this, if true, would probably not impale them. Isaac Newton might have supported the suggestion that apples fall from trees with sufficient force to impale themselves, but a hedgehog sitting below is, like Sir Isaac, not expecting random events such as being struck by falling apples. And, in the normal course of relaxed activity or rest, the hedgehog keeps its spines laying flat, not bristling. Falling apples then bounce off, whether they drop on to hedgehogs or distinguished eighteenth-century scientists. Even supposing a hedgehog did manage to pick up an apple, getting another one would be doubly difficult and making off with a whole back full of booty (as in medieval pictures) stretches probability too far.

*Medieval drawings of hedgehogs carrying apples*

However, the biggest doubts must centre on why the hedgehog would bother at all. When it needs to carry things (e.g. nest building material), it uses its mouth not its spines. Moreover, it has no need to carry fruit at all; it can eat it and any associated slugs and insects right where it lies on the ground. Hedgehogs do not take food back to the nest to feed their young. Nor do they hoard food for the winter as hibernating rodents do: they store their winter energy supply in the form of fat. Of all the hundreds of times I have examined hedgehog winter nests I have never once found anything which might have constituted a hedgehog's larder. If hedgehogs did carry fruit, why don't they similarly make off with bits of bread and milk or roll on worms and slugs to pick them up?

It's a nice story, but it won't do! When the issue was aired on a television programme seen by over 12 million viewers, the BBC was not deluged with first-hand 20th-century observations of fruit-carrying, and so we must conclude that the case is 'not proven'.

## Hedgehogs in folklore: taking milk from cows

A favourite country tale is that hedgehogs suck milk from cows. This story has a ring of truth about it, albeit a muffled one. Hedgehogs certainly like cow's milk and will rarely ignore a chance to partake of it; but obviously if the cow is standing up the hedgehog is too short to help itself. When cows lie down, their teats are within reach and often ooze milk, droplets of which may spatter the nearby grass advertising availability to any passing hedgehogs. Leakage of milk is most probable when the udder is full after a night's grazing. Thus, hedgehogs are most likely to find milk in the early morning, when the cows are lying down waiting to be called in to the milking shed. It is exactly at this time that the cowhand appears on the scene to fetch the cows and may spot a slurping hedgehog.

So this is a story that could be true, up to a point. It's unlikely that a hedgehog could actually suck from a cow. Its mouth does not open wide enough to encompass the average teat and even if it did, the cow would probably react indignantly to the hedgehog's teeth. It is interesting that a veterinary research journal reported a few years ago

that teat damage had been observed which was consistent with the peculiar size and shape of hedgehog teeth. Maybe some hedgehogs occasionally push their luck a bit far.

## Hedgehogs in folklore: proof against snakebite?

It has long been suggested that hedgehogs are immune to the bite of snakes. One major Russian zoologist even went so far as to say that this enables hedgehogs to prey extensively on serpents and that a shortage of snakes in some areas may be a major cause of hedgehog scarcity!

It is true that hedgehogs are resistant to a snake's bite, but perhaps not to its venom. The distinction is important. In Britain, our only poisonous snake is the adder; there are other poisonous species on the Continent but none is very large. In every case the fangs are shorter than a hedgehog's spines. So, when investigators in the past (not me) set up a gladiatorial contest between hedgehog and snake, they observed the snake striking in a series of futile attacks against the spiny armour of the hedgehog. Not only do the fangs fail to reach the skin underneath and cause any harm, but the bristling spines could inflict mortal injury on the snake, which then suffers multiple perforations. Moreover, if the hedgehog responds by biting the snake, the snake jerks and the hedgehog rolls up. If it still has a grip on the reptile, the hedgehog will then be rolled up around it, exerting all the force of its rolling up muscles to stretch the snake and force further spines into it. The action is automatic, not deliberate, and very effective (if you are holding a hedgehog and it suddenly rolls up, trapping your fingers inside the spiny ball, you get a very uncomfortable insight into the fate of the luckless snake). The result of these conflicts is often death or disablement of the snake, and the hedgehog may follow up its triumph by making a meal of its foe.

Thus far the folk story appears true. However, should the snake manage a lucky strike on the hedgehog's unprotected face or leg, where the skin is quite thin, a dose of venom can be delivered which will make the hedgehog very ill or even kill it in a few hours. However, more scientific tests on resistance to experimentally injected doses of poison suggest that hedgehogs are indeed more resistant than some other common animals, but hedgehogs are not immune to snake venom.

Research in Sweden takes the story a bit further. Tests with hedgehog blood (not whole hedgehogs) show that snake venom does less damage to hedgehog blood cells than to the blood of other species. So hedgehogs really do have a degree of resistance to snake poison. This is curious because immunity ought to have evolved only if it was useful for a hedgehog to be protected in this way. Yet as hedgehogs are nocturnal, and snakes are not, it is hard to imagine them coming into contact sufficiently often for such a mechanism to have evolved.

Under the special circumstances of hibernation, hedgehogs are observed to be extraordinarily resistant to many poisonous substances. They are able to survive massive overdoses of poisons that would kill much larger animals several times over. Hibernating hedgehogs can also survive half an hour in poisonous carbon monoxide gas; they are even abnormally unaffected by ionizing radiation. However, these hardly constitute natural threats in the wild; the hedgehog's surprising ability to cheat death while it is in hibernation is of only academic interest rather than real use in the everyday world. Although it would be true to say that a hibernating hedgehog would not be killed by a snake's bite, this is again purely academic. If the hedgehog was in hibernation, the snake would be too.

# Island hedgehogs: the North Ronaldsay Saga

North Ronaldsay is a small island in the Orkneys, lying to the north of Scotland. It was engulfed by ice during the last Ice Age, and by the time that had melted, sea levels had risen and prevented colonisation by land animals like hedgehogs. The same process kept a lot of the Scottish islands free of terrestrial predators until humans carried them there and released different things in different places, creating the present-day assortment of species on various islands. Meanwhile, the predator-free islands had proved safe havens for large numbers of ground-nesting birds.

Hedgehogs were taken to North Ronaldsay in 1972, and released into a gardener's greenhouse to control pests. Apparently there were only three of them, but needless to say they soon got out and prospered mightily. I began to get letters and phone calls about declining bird populations and the hedgehogs were blamed for taking the eggs of birds that had previously nested for centuries free of such dangers. It seemed unlikely that so few hedgehogs could have become sufficiently numerous to do so much damage. I was rather sceptical, especially as some of the declining birds, fulmars for example, normally nest on cliff ledges! Nevertheless, there was much publicity and newspapers carried stories about there being 10,000 hedgehogs, an impossible figure bearing in mind that the species had only been present for ten years. A more scientifically based estimate by Hugh Warwick put the number at 400-600 in 1986, still a surprisingly large number after so short a time on the island.

Eventually a few dozen were rounded up and deported to mainland Scotland, amidst much hysterical attention. I even had a long phone call about it from a Japanese TV station in Tokyo asking what was going on and please could they come and film me (although I had nothing to do with the story!). In fact the hedgehogs never really became very numerous and have since declined sharply in numbers. The failure of breeding in the bird colonies was also observed in other islands where there were no hedgehogs. It was actually due to collapse of the sand eel populations upon which the birds feed,

nothing to do with hedgehogs. The North Ronaldsay case is a salutary example of the dangers of jumping to conclusions. It also shows that introduced populations may enjoy a few years of abundance and then decline naturally, something that has been seen elsewhere with other introduced mammals. Both lessons had apparently been forgotten by 2003, when attempts began to remove them from the Uists (see p. 186). In the 1960s, hedgehogs used to be a problem raiding bird's nests at Dungeness on the Kent coast, but they had apparently almost all gone by the 1980s. The birds are still abundant there. Maybe it's better to leave things alone and not overreact to short-term events?

# Keeping things in perspective

As with the raiding of pheasant and partridge nests (see p. 65), it is important to make sure that the right culprits are identified and to keep the damage in perspective. For example, a colony of black headed gulls in Cumbria used to lose quite a lot of newly hatched chicks to hungry hedgehogs, but it was a huge colony. The loss was small (about 8%) in comparison with the total number of chicks produced; foxes took 46% of the chicks killed by predators. Moreover, the gulls themselves were cannibals and ate twice as many chicks as did the hedgehogs.

# Island hedgehogs – the Uist problem

North and South Uist are part of the Hebridean islands, off the west coast of Scotland. They are home to about 17,000 pairs of wading birds, notably redshanks and dunlin that come to the islands in summer to breed, safe from mainland predators. About a quarter of the entire British breeding population of dunlin and ringed plover nest there. The islands had no hedgehogs until 1974, when four were taken there to control garden pests, with another three added the following year. They prospered and by 2002 hedgehogs were officially estimated to number at least 5,000, having enjoyed high survival rates and prolific breeding. Meanwhile, wader numbers had declined, particularly where hedgehogs were present. Careful study showed that many nests were being destroyed by egg-eating predators, particularly hedgehogs. Removing hedgehogs from small areas resulted in increased nesting success. Clearly there was a 'hedgehog problem' and a prominent conservationist was even quoted in the *Sunday Times* advocating the killing of hedgehogs with poison baits as a means of saving the birds from extinction.

One might dispute the seriousness of bird losses on the grounds that they had been unusually abundant in the past, but hedgehogs were not a natural part of the islands' fauna and should take second place. Moreover, the EU Birds Directive requires action to be taken to protect these birds (although hedgehogs do not enjoy similar official protection). The issue was what to do about them. Scottish Natural Heritage (SNH) is ultimately responsible for wildlife conservation on the islands and decided to attempt the eradication of the hedgehog population by capture and humane destruction. This decision was opposed by 'Uist Hedgehog Rescue' (UHR), a group of voluntary organisations, representing the widespread public support that hedgehogs enjoy. UHR accepted that hedgehogs were a problem and should be removed, but argued that they should not be killed. Instead they could be captured and taken to the mainland to be released alive.

SNH decided to kill the hedgehogs, rather than move them, because they said that translocated hedgehogs might suffer in some unspecified way. It was claimed that the animals might have a 'low quality' of life and suffer starvation, injury or illness, but these assertions completely ignore the results of my studies of translocated hedgehogs, which show substantial survival rates even among animals that have spent long periods in captivity and have no previous experience of life in the wild (see p. 100). If rehabilitated sick and injured hedgehogs (even juveniles) can survive for over a year, and some for more than three years, then healthy adult animals from the Uists should manage perfectly well too. It was also claimed that there might be 'disease problems', but nobody seemed able to actually name a disease that might be involved, and anyway the animals had come from the mainland in the first place. The claim (without evidence) that, because some individuals might suffer as a result of translocation from the Uists, all must be killed attracted widespread public condemnation. It's a bit like saying that because some sick people might suffer if they are taken to hospital, they are all better off dead. There was a big outcry and an official petition was considered by the Scottish Parliament.

Nevertheless, in 2003, 2004 and 2005, SNH employed staff to collect hedgehogs and humanely kill them. Capture was limited to a

*Hedgehog raiding the nest of a redshank*

six-week 'window' in April and May because most animals would be still hibernating earlier than that and continuing later might result in killing nursing females and consequent starvation of their young.

This process was opposed by the UHR consortium, whose volunteer teams attempted to catch and translocate as many animals as possible as an alternative to their being killed. This activity received widespread public support, including donations totalling tens of thousands of pounds. Some of this was spent paying local people £20 a head for each hedgehog they brought in, and one local gamekeeper (nicknamed 'the Pimpernel' in the press) was reported to have earned £1,000 rescuing hedgehogs. The newspapers made a big story of this extravagance, but the SNH staff caught fewer hedgehogs in 2005 than the rescuers and, because of high staffing costs (£62,000 of public money), their hedgehogs worked out at over £340 each, a point that seems to have been overlooked by supposedly money-conscious Scottish taxpayers!

There were demands from hedgehog supporters to test the repeated claim that animals removed from the Uists might suffer unacceptably and die, but SNH insisted on a huge and complex investigation, full of statistical rigour, and then refused to meet even part of the cost. The UHR consortium, using public donations, undertook to follow up what happened to a small sample of animals transferred from the Uists in April 2005 to a country park south of Glasgow. Twenty female hedgehogs were used because females travel less far each night, making it possible to monitor a larger sample than if males had been included. They were radio tracked and weighed each night for four weeks. There were at least nine wild male hedgehogs present on the study site and they must have enjoyed having twice that number of females delivered to them right at the start of the breeding season! Eleven of the released females were found consorting with wild males at various times, often on several occasions. There was no sign of any aggressive reaction to the newcomers from the local hedgehogs.

The animals had gained weight substantially during the initial period following capture, suggesting that the stress of being caught, transported and confined to a tiny cage for up to three weeks was not sufficient to give rise to significant welfare concerns. Two of the released animals were lost to predators (either dog or badger), three others fell

*Ringed plover doing 'broken wing' display to distract hedgehog*

ill and were taken back into captivity and one simply disappeared. Twelve out of the twenty animals maintained their body weights after release, or increased them significantly, despite the unfamiliar terrain. If those lost accidentally are excluded, plus the one that had an existing tumour, the survival rate was 75%, successfully translocated from the Uists to the mainland. Natural mortality, especially among yearlings, must be high soon after winter and translocation could add to their problems. April is a challenging time for hedgehogs anyway, with depleted fat reserves insufficient to cope with unpredictable weather affecting food availability. Nevertheless, the rescued animals managed well. There was no evidence of suffering as a result of being transported to the mainland.

Another study was also carried out independently of ours and with a larger number of hedgehogs. This confirmed all our previous research showing that hedgehogs that had been moved from one place to another, or released from captivity, can manage perfectly well. It also suggested that hedgehogs rescued from the Uists did better if they spent a short while in captivity before being released. This allows them to build up fat reserves before being moved to a new place and is particularly important because the Uist animals were caught almost immediately they emerged from hibernation, with fat reserves perilously low. Our rescued animals enjoyed a higher survival rate than in the other study, whose hedgehogs had been released into a suburban habitat in Bristol. Ours were released in a Scottish park, which was not climatically or ecologically too dissimilar to the Uist environment. Bristol gardens, with their multitude of unfamiliar noises, street lights and especially scents from cats, dogs, foxes and other animals, must have come as a bit of a shock to the translocated hedgehogs. As our study in Suffolk suggested, hedgehogs are probably better off if released in a similar type of habitat than that from which they have been removed.

The policy of killing Uist hedgehogs rather than translocating them to the mainland was also based on the principle that if the mainland could support more hedgehogs then it would do so naturally, and any additional animals would result in corresponding mortality in existing populations because there would be insufficient food to go round. Our study offers no support for this idea. If food was a limiting factor, then none of our animals should have maintained or gained weight, but twelve of them did. Anyway, whatever natural mechanisms have evolved over 20 million years to govern hedgehog numbers, new 'predation', in the form of motor vehicles and mowing machines, has emerged within only a few decades, too short a time for a successful evolutionary response to develop. Releasing rescued hedgehogs may not disrupt natural mechanisms at all, but might helpfully make up for the many thousands of hedgehogs that die from these new and unnatural causes. Insisting that translocation of hedgehogs from problem areas such as the Uists might involve welfare problems is not justified by our studies. Killing hedgehogs when they are captured might spare a few from suffering, but at the expense of the majority that could have lived. Translocating problem animals might help to boost declining hedgehog populations on the mainland, but killing them certainly will not. SNH nevertheless insist that the killing will continue.

# Island hedgehogs – the Uist 'solution'?

The controversy over the Uist hedgehogs will not go away, but why make all that fuss about what to do with them when nobody has yet worked out how to catch them all? Catching the first 95% of the population is the easy bit. Getting the last few is really hard, yet eradication requires that every one must go because the whole problem began with less than ten animals.

In the 2004 catching season, volunteers and SNH combined captured just under 500 hedgehogs in total. If the total population is 5,000 (SNH's own estimate), this represents only a 10% cull. It is highly unlikely that this (or any other) population can be eradicated by such a low removal rate, and certainly not in a reasonable length of time. If the remaining animals conveniently fail to breed (unlikely!) it would still take ten years to remove them all. Meanwhile the cost goes up because as the numbers fall, the remaining hogs get harder to find. In order to maintain a catch of 500 per year, you then need more catchers and more expense, especially if catching continues to be limited to only six weeks of the year.

The hedgehogs were captured by hand, using powerful torches at night. But this is not easy, particularly in rough terrain or where every grass tussock looks like a hedgehog from a distance. On average, only one hedgehog was found for every man-hour spent searching even when hedgehogs were most numerous. Clearly, if the plan was going to work, catching had to become much more efficient than now. The best way to do this is to get the help of some dogs. However, as part of the ban on fox hunting, it is now illegal to use dogs to flush out wild mammals except where the animals are shot immediately, and this was now proposed as the way forward. SNH announced plans to use dogs to find the animals in their nests, extract the hedgehogs by hand, and then blow them away with a shotgun while they are rolled up. This extension of the Uist hedgehog saga seems not only absurd, but also dangerous and highly distasteful. That seems also to have

dawned on SNH, who scrapped the idea soon after suggesting it.

As a result of our studies, the killing was called off, but if this ill-founded project fails to eradicate hedgehogs, large amounts of public money will have been wasted and annual culls will still be required. In 2005 killing hedgehogs cost £62,000, £344 for each dead one. There was little evidence to show that bird numbers had benefited, so efforts need to be increased, resulting in still higher costs. What a waste - of hedgehogs and public money. Experience elsewhere (on North Ronaldsay for example) suggests that populations of newly-introduced animals boom and then collapse. Maybe if the Uists were left alone the problem would sort itself out in time. Meanwhile, hedgehogs should not be taken to islands where they do not occur naturally.

# Hedgehogs in the news

Hedgehog stories often turn up in the newspapers. In case you missed them, here is a small selection to help keep you in touch with what has been going on in the world of hedgehogs.

In 1997, a self-styled 'King of the Gypsies' was said to be organising a barbecue at which hedgehogs marinated in honey and stuffed with shrimps were to be served at a cost of £12.50 per head. Up to 500 people were expected to attend. The event was cancelled after massive protests from the British Hedgehog Preservation Society, among many others.

The *Manx Independent* carried a report (29 April 1995) about a local woman who was photographed in her wedding dress holding two hedgehogs. She took them to her wedding reception so that they could continue to be fed regularly.

There have been several newspaper accounts of bloodthirsty hedgehogs attacking other animals including a live frog, ducklings and one hedgehog attempting to slaughter a live blackbird. The *Oban Times* (6 October 1994) reported that 'Killer Hedgehogs' were on the loose in the area, based on someone finding a couple of them eating bantam chicks. A local gamekeeper generously took the blame, owning up to feeding hedgehogs on chicken flavoured dog foods which, it was suggested, might have given the animals a taste for fowl. This led other readers to write to the newspaper, each advancing an even more preposterous tale. One woman claimed she had 'gigantic' hedgehogs, 'as big as a Labrador', coming into her kitchen to devour her cats. She added with a shudder that 'One was so big I had to call for help to escape from it'. Another imaginative local reported sheep being savaged by hedgehogs. Maybe there's something odd in the drinking water around Oban?

Another newspaper story headed 'Mark of Bad Taste' reported that a storm of local protest had caused a Devonshire supermarket owner to stop selling concrete models of squashed hedgehogs with a tyre mark across their back. Evidently his sense of humour was not universally appreciated.

The *Yorkshire Post* (March 1985) carried a story about a grass fire near Rotherham. It appears that one of the firemen found a badly singed hedgehog as a result of treading on it. The animal was christened 'Charcoal' and taken to the RSPCA. A spokesman for the Mexborough Fire Brigade said it was 'all part of the service'.

According to *The Independent*, (22 August 1996) a 'protest artist' had been collecting squashed hedgehogs off the roads dipping them in clay and firing them in an oven to make weatherproof effigies in the positions in which they had died. The ceramic animals would then be taken back to the place where they had been killed, as a protest against wanton slaughter of wildlife by motor cars.

In April 1985 the government sharply increased road taxes and still more tax was added to the cost of petrol. The *Guardian* reported this story under the heading 'keeping the car in the garage'. An accompanying cartoon showed two hedgehogs greeting this news by dancing with joy.

Down in Wales a man bought a brand new Ford Sierra, but was then puzzled to hear scratching noises from within the dashboard (*Daily Express*, October 1983). An electrician dismantled the dash and found a hedgehog living there, 'very reluctant to come out'. The car had been made in Belgium and it was suspected that the animal had been put inside as a joke. If so, it was cruel because the animal was not discovered until the autumn. Moreover its import was in breach of regulations aimed at keeping animals in quarantine to avoid importing rabies to Britain. However, it is unlikely it had survived all summer without food, and more probable that somehow the animal had got into the car after its arrival here.

The *Bognor Regis Observer* (16 May 1991) reported the sad case of a hedgehog that had gone round the bend – literally. Somehow it got into a lavatory pan and lodged in the U bend, where it stopped the flow of water and other materials. After much effort, the owners finally disconnected the pan and took it outside, where they broke it open to liberate the unfortunate beast. It died just a day after its rescue. Shame about the lavatory pan.

A story in the *Daily Telegraph* (12 May 1990) claimed that Britain's biggest colony of Little Terns nesting on the beach at Great Yarmouth had been 'largely wiped out' by two hedgehogs and a kestrel. It didn't mention the thousands of visitors and their dogs that swarm on these popular beaches every summer ...

*Woman's Own* (10 November 1984) told the story of a lady who stopped her car to rescue a large hedgehog leading two small babies across the road. She carried the animal to the verge and knelt down to pick up the other two, then realised that they were actually lumps of horse manure!

In 2001 a baby was born in St Peter's Hospital, Shepton Mallet, and subsequently given the distinctive name of 'Ebenezer Hedgehog Crinklebum'. Major Adrian Coles of the British Hedgehog Preservation Society commented that 'hedgehog' was an excellent name and 'showed good judgement and discernment'.

# Hedgehog research

I am often asked what sort of research is being done on hedgehogs and have to confess that it's very little. Laboratory studies have investigated aspects of breeding and hibernation and some field work has been done to look at various ecological topics. My own studies and those of my students represent a very small effort that barely scratches the surface. For example we have looked at home range, feeding and hibernation in parkland, farmland and on a suburban golf course (because working in the dark in open grassy habitats is fairly easy) but these are rather peculiar habitats. Behaviour and activities might be quite different elsewhere.

The technical problems of working on hedgehogs are very considerable; worse is the difficulty of studying a nocturnal animal when our own lives are geared to daytime work. You can't do both and a few nights out with the hedgehogs plays havoc with your social life, not to mention any other daytime work you are supposed to do. But the main problem is money. Because the hedgehog is not an endangered species or a serious economic pest, it gets overlooked. Money is directed towards studying other more deserving (though better understood) species. There isn't a lot of research money about and even the smallest study costs an extraordinary amount. In our 4-week investigation of hedgehogs and food bowls, we drove 26 miles a day: over 600 miles in all. The students who did the donkey work each put in 6 hours or more per night (non-stop, no meals or tea breaks), totalling 400+ man-hours. Any kind of reasonable payment soon runs up a big bill, even without counting the cost of equipment (radio transmitters cost £100 each for example, and receivers ten times as much), torch batteries, computer time and so on. A full time research assistant of the cheapest kind costs over £15,000 per year without paying for vehicle costs or equipment. Who's going to spend that much on hedgehogs?

Fortunately the British Hedgehog Preservation Society, The People's Trust for Endangered Species and the RSPCA have all contributed towards my studies, but money has always been a major limitation. I once received a donation from a Mrs Coulthard-Bayley in memory of her late husband who loved wildlife. I spent the money on a computer programme that helped to analyse radio-tracking data and to train generations of students in the use of computers in wildlife fieldwork, in the days when that was relatively novel. It was the best investment I ever made of such a small sum. Sadly, when I wrote a couple of years later to report progress, my letter was returned, marked 'gone away'.

It is frustrating to hear of yet another donkey inheriting a nice farm when its owner dies, or thousands of pounds being left to a cat in someone's will. I don't begrudge these bequests or condemn their well meaning owners for making them. However, wild animals need help too, often a lot more. People seem willing to accept this for birds, and provide substantial gifts and bequests. I hope this book has helped make the case for doing the same for hedgehogs too, through the Hedgehog Preservation Society or even as used notes in a paper bag straight to me! Seriously, we should not assume that someone else will take care of our wildlife. We must not take our common and much loved mammals for granted. They need help and understanding, based on sound research. Otherwise many of them might well cease to be common and future generations will not be able to enjoy them as we have done.

# The hedgehog's future – has it got one?

Much of what has been said earlier in this book suggests that hedgehogs are in trouble and their populations are declining. At least the problems with cumulative pesticides are now a thing of the past, and perhaps gamekeepers are less of a problem too. However, this is probably balanced by the increase in hungry badgers and the ever-present toll taken by road traffic.

Suppose you could go to your local park and see a woolly mammoth or visit the zoo to view a sabre toothed tiger! That would be really amazing wouldn't it? These are prehistoric creatures, consigned to museum cupboards and the dustbin of history. But the hedgehog is an even more ancient animal that obligingly comes to our own gardens, but we give it scarcely a second thought. It's not even listed on the British government's current national Biodiversity Action Plan (although badgers are!). We are in danger of taking hedgehogs for granted.

They and their ancestors have been pottering about for 20 million years, more than twice as long as the woolly mammoth, but for how much longer? There is good news and bad, often all mixed up as is the way with the complexity of modern wildlife issues. Hedgehogs have one huge advantage over many other animals – they are popular with humans. No matter how much we dominate the world, it seems we want 'hogs to share it with us. Opinion surveys consistently show hedgehogs among the top ten most popular animals, at least in Britain (and increasingly so across the rest of western Europe). They appear trusting and confiding creatures, perhaps we respond by being caring and supportive.

People care about hedgehogs and want to help them. We feel sorry for this bumbling animal as it shuffles about our modern world. We all know it and perhaps feel slightly guilty at the sight of the pathetic flattened remains of a hedgehog dead on the road. Having adjusted to its environment over millions of years, the hedgehog has had to contend with traffic in just a single century. The bristling spiny defence

*Oh, bad luck, Bertie.*

that saved generations of hedgehogs from most natural predators is no protection from four big wheels travelling at 60mph! Even newer threats come from the proliferation of mowing machines and strimmers. These don't just cut the grass, but also chop up sleeping hedgehogs. The danger is clearly focused on hedgehogs using the long vegetation as their home. Other animals would flee to safety, but the hedgehog lies there motionless relying naively on its spines for protection.

The good news is that increasing numbers of injured and sickly hedgehogs are nowadays cared for by a whole network of wildlife care centres and well meaning people. More good news comes from our studies which show that released hedgehog manage surprisingly well. Although some rehabilitated hedgehogs will be killed soon after release, at least they got a second chance, better than dying first time round! Those that do survive may breed, keeping numbers up, something they could not have done if they had not been rescued in the first place.

Today's countryside is increasingly smothered by industrial development and housing, with plans for millions of new homes to be built on farmland. Perhaps this is not all bad and the future may offer more gardens, with more food put out for wildlife by their owners? The problem here is that most new gardens are too small. Hedgehogs normally wander widely: an average home range is about 90,000 square metres. Most newly created housing areas have gardens of less than 90 square metres. Nevertheless, if the habitat is right and the animals can move freely between gardens they may be OK. However, the habitat is often poor – a concrete patio, a trimmed lawn soaked in chemicals to eradicate worms and perhaps a garden pond in which hedgehogs may drown. Flowerbeds have a much lower biodiversity than comparable areas of natural habitat, and are kept that way by 'weeding' and use of more chemicals including slug pellets, a potential threat to wildlife, both in gardens and on farmland crops.

Most modern gardens are too tidy, with nowhere to build a secure nest or natural materials to make it with. Although hedgehogs can climb surprisingly well, free movement between gardens is often prevented by smooth wooden fencing resting on a concrete base. Indeed, fences, walls and concrete barriers along roads are another modern wildlife threat that is rarely recognised. Barriers to movement prevent the animals from dispersing and breeding freely. Instead, small isolated populations exist, becoming inbred and at risk from chance extinction with no prospect of reinvasion by immigrants. It is common for people to say they used to have hedgehogs in their gardens, but they come no longer. This is probably because once the regulars have died, fresh ones cannot spread in because of newly created walls, wider roads and other barriers to dispersal. Piecemeal extinction through fragmentation of habitats is a modern threat to all wildlife, but its effects are not widely understood and difficult to predict – until too late.

Another knotty problem for the future concerns badgers. This is the only real predator that hedgehogs have. Its claws are long enough to reach through the hedgehog's spines, and the limb muscles powerful enough to tear it apart. In the past badgers were sufficiently scarce that relatively few hedgehogs were lost this way. However, badger numbers have nearly doubled in recent years, and are already high enough to threaten the survival of hedgehogs in many parts of England. Even if the badgers never touch hedgehogs, they still eat many of the same worms and invertebrates. The extra 100,000 badgers we have gained in the past half century effectively do half a million hedgehogs out of their food. More badgers must mean less of something else and hedgehogs seem likely to suffer as a result.

Perhaps the biggest factor is changes in the countryside and the way it is used. Pastures, bounded by hedges, provide ideal hedgehog habitat, with easy feeding in the dung-enriched short turf and secure nesting places in the nearby hedges. Modern farms, with few hedges and arable crops dosed with chemicals to kill off the vital beetles, worms, slugs and other vital prey, offer little support for hedgehogs. But more change is on its way. Reform of the EU Common Agricultural Policy has already shifted subsidies away from intensive farming, and this trend is likely to continue. Large parts of the future countryside are likely to be 're-wilded' and revert to more natural states. Tree planting has become very fashionable and newly planted areas offer good hedgehog habitat, if there are any left to use it. However, woodland is not so good for hedgehogs as grazed farmland, with nearby hedges and bushes for nesting. But grazing is in decline.

So, there will be a future, but what it will mean for the hedgehog is far from clear and not altogether hopeful. The important thing is that people should know and understand more about wildlife ecology and the effects of change. They can then express a view on what sort of countryside and towns they want for the future, instead of just letting things happen and then regretting the effects afterwards. The one thing we can be certain of, as a French philosopher said, ''tis Nature's way to change, constancy alone is strange'.

# Further reading

Because there has been little research on hedgehogs there's been little to write about. Hence there are few 'popular' books available. Most of the detailed studies of hedgehogs have been published as short papers in scientific journals, so are not easily available to most folk. The following books can be purchased or obtained via a local library, but several are long out of print and unlikely to be found except in second-hand bookshops.

K. Bullen, *Hedgehog Rehabilitation* (British Hedgehog Preservation Society, Ludlow, 2002) - a very useful handbook.
M. Burton, *The Hedgehog* (Andre Deutsch, London, 1969)
S. Harris and D. W. Yalden, *Mammals of the British Isles, Handbook 4th Edition.* (The Mammal Society, Southampton, 2008)
K. Herter, *Hedgehogs* (Phoenix House, London, 1965)
P. A. Morris, *The Hedgehog* (Shire Publications, Princes Risborough, 1988)
N. Reeve, *The Natural History of Hedgehogs* (Academic Press, London, 1994) - a comprehensive review of hedgehog studies
L. Sykes and J. Durrant, *The Natural Hedgehog* (Gaia Books, London, 1995)
H. Warwick, *A Prickly Affair* (Allen Lane, London, 2008) - an informative and highly entertaining book!

There have been other books published, several based heavily on the one you have just read.

# Information

The British Hedgehog Preservation Society, founded by Major Adrian Coles in 1982, has been promoting research on hedgehogs, assisting hedgehog carers and raising the profile of hedgehogs and the issues they highlight. They distribute a Newsletter to friends of the hedgehog and offer a fun 'Hogalogue' catalogue of all sorts of hoggery from notepaper and cards to nest boxes and hoggy toys. They are the best point of contact if you need advice, for example on where to find your nearest hedgehog hospital. The address is: British Hedgehog Preservation Society, Hedgehog House, Dhustone, Clee Hill, Ludlow, Shropshire SY8 3PL. Tel : 01584 890 801 Website: www.britishhedgehogs.org.uk

The Mammal Society (3 The Carronades, Southampton SO14 0AA, website www.mammal.org.uk) is a national organization which seeks to promote the study of mammals. Membership includes professional biologists, teachers and also non-biologists with an interest in mammals. A Youth Group caters for the under 18s. The society issues a Newsletter to members 4 times a year, the journal Mammal Review and has meetings at least twice a year.

The Mammals Trust (UK) and the Peoples Trust for Endangered Species (Cloisters House, 8 Battersea Park Road, London SW8 4BG, website http://www.mtuk.org) support many mammal conservation projects and related research. They are also responsible for the Mammals on Roads surveys, which remain our best tool for monitoring the changing numbers of hedgehogs.

The County Wildlife Trusts (address from your local library) support and co-ordinate wildlife conservation at a local level.

Typing 'Hedgehog' into an internet search engine will show about three million 'hits', so there is no shortage of information out there! For example, hedgehogcentral.com will take you to lots of chat rooms and information from the American pet hedgehog fraternity and you can link up with Swedish hedghoggers too via http://hem.passagen.se/hedgehogs/hedgehogs.html. Then there's the International hedgehog Association (http://hedgehogclub.com/), not to mention the Hedgehog Rock Band and hedgehog stuff on the eBay internet auction site. Various hedgehog watchers have their own home pages and so do many hedgehog carers and specialist animal hospitals.

# Index

food 29, 35, 40, 41, 62-6, 78, 89, 90, 93, 94-8, 99, 101, 105, 109, 111, 115-124, 130, 134, 135, 136, 142, 143, 149, 151, 159, 161, 162, 163, 181, 191
footprints 28
fur 17, 31, 32, 33, 48, 49 *see also* hair

gamekeepers 65, 150, 151, 152-5, 162, 175, 199
garden hedgehogs 21, 22, 25, 75, 91, 101, 111-113, 115-124, 127, 129, 149, 151, 201
gardens 22, 74-6, 101, 104, 111-113, 116, 117, 118, 201
gestation 84
growth 11, 122, 135

habitat 17, 19, 20, 22, 104, 112, 142, 148, 169, 191, 197, 201
hair 27, 29, 30, 31, 32, 33, 40, 47, 67
handling 54, 83, 94, 99
hibernation 25, 45, 55, 84, 89, 97, 100, 109, 134-9, 141, 142-5, 156, 158, 162, 178, 184
home range 76-7, 104, 148, 197, 201
homing 102

introductions 18, 19, 20

learning 44-6
legal protection 152, 176
legislation 175-6
lifespan 156-7

litter size 25

maggots on skin 49, 51
marking hedgehogs 125-8
mating 31, 79-82
metaldehyde 129-132
moult 33, 86

names 10
nest 49, 74-5, 86-8, 90, 91, 94, 98, 102, 105, 106, 109, 112, 116, 118, 120, 122, 139, 140-146, 150, 191, 201
nest boxes 114
New Zealand 17, 24-6, 49, 55, 150, 169
nocturnality 39, 55, 77-8

parasites 47-50, 52-3, 75
persecution 152-155, 175-6, 185-193
pesticides 130, 151, 163-4, 199
poisons 132-3, 163, 184
population cycles 150, 156, 174
population size 147-151, 159, 168, 199
predators 58, 59, 77, 109, 152, 153, 157, 159-161, 171
pregnancy 84, 85

rabies 54, 195
radio tracking 70, 71, 72, 74, 110, 113, 116, 148, 151, 170, 198
recognising individual hedgehogs 124-8
release into the wild 20, 38, 52,